The Control of Human Heredity and Evolution

The Control of Human Heredity and Evolution

Edited by T. M. SONNEBORN

Professor of Zoology
Indiana University
Bloomington, Indiana

The Macmillan Company, New York
Collier–Macmillan, Limited, London

First Printing

Library of Congress catalog card number: 65-12149

THE MACMILLAN COMPANY, NEW YORK
COLLIER-MACMILLAN CANADA, LTD.,
TORONTO, ONTARIO

Printed in the United States of America

Dedication

To the memory of H. S. Jennings (1868-1944),
father of the genetics of unicellular organisms
and leading educator of the general public
of his generation in the bearing of
biological, and chiefly genetic,
knowledge on human affairs.

Preface

Thirty-three years ago Aldous Huxley published a widely read book about the possible impact of the rapidly developing life sciences on man. It set people of that generation to thinking about the life sciences and what they might do to and for man. *Brave New World* is a fanciful story of what human life might be like in the year A.F. 600, that is, 600 years After Ford, the symbol of mass production. Among other things, Huxley imagined mass production of test-tube babies of types and in numbers set by the rulers of the state. The types of babies and the kinds of people they developed into were controlled by combining eugenic selection with a few embryological tricks, and the action of applied hormones, drugs, and psychological conditioning.

Fifteen years later, after the atomic bomb, Huxley remarked:

> The theme of *Brave New World* is not the advancement of science as such; it is the advancement of science as it affects human individuals. The triumphs of physics, chemistry and engineering are tacitly taken for granted. . . . It is only by means of the sciences of life that the quality of life can be radically changed. The sciences of matter can be applied in such a way that they will destroy life or make the living of it impossibly complex and uncomfortable; but, unless used as instruments by the biologists and psychologists, they can do nothing to modify the natural forms and expressions of life itself. The release of atomic energy marks a great revolution in human history, but not (unless we blow ourselves to bits and so put an end to history) the final and most searching revolution. The really revolutionary revolution is to be achieved, not in the external world, but in the souls and flesh of human beings.

Another 15 years and a little more have now passed. In that brief span, biology has undergone a revolution the scope and impact of which not even the penetrating imagination of Aldous Huxley could sense, although the seeds of it had already been sown when Huxley made those remarks. New possibilities of controlling human development have emerged. The hormone and drug techniques envisaged by Huxley are superficial by comparison. They treat symptoms; the new techniques could aim at the basic physical causes. Even more drastic a change has come about in regard to possibilities of controlling the initial hereditary endowment of people. Besides selecting existing kinds of parents, directly making the desired hereditary endowment and other radically new procedures are now foreseen by some as possibilities.

The human problems raised by these new possibilities are not fundamentally different from the problems Huxley put forcibly before the public. They are problems of morals, ethics, religion, and politics. They are problems of how knowledge, and the power that knowledge confers, will be used. They could be used for good or for ill, for the enslavement or the liberation of man. How they will be used obviously will not be decided by scientists alone. Nor should this be decided alone by professional politicians or by theologians or by philosophers or by moralists. It should be decided by an enlightened and broadly based public opinion.

To help contribute toward its formation, this symposium was designed. We biologists who are aware of the facts and their possible human implications conceive it to be our responsibility to expose these facts and implications to the public in as intelligible a way as we can, to discuss them publicly among ourselves, and to urge the public to assume its responsibility of contributing as wisely as it can to the formation of public policy.

But why the urgency? If Huxley estimated 600 years until his lesser prophecies would be fulfilled, why bother now to form judgments about even more extreme and perhaps more remote possibilities? Interestingly, in 1946 Huxley pared his 1931 estimate of 600 years down to 100 years. So rapidly is the pace of science accelerating that some of the newer prophets proclaim that the new and more extreme applications to man may be just around the corner.

I am not one of those who think the radical applications are so imminent. After thinking the matter through as well as I could, I came two years ago to the conclusion that great technical impasses and vast areas of ignorance would have to be overcome first. How long that will take, if it is done at all, is hazardous to guess. If it will not be a short time, man is lucky, for he will need all the time he can have to wrestle with the tremendous ethical, moral, religious, and political problems posed by the possibility of controlling the direction of human heredity and evolution.

From what our several authors write, you will see that well-informed and thoughtful biologists can come to different judgments about the situation. They differ as to their guesses on how long it will be before human heredity can be directly controlled. They differ as to their judgments of the extent to which it will ever be controllable. Because of these differences, they stress different approaches, especially for the immediate future. In other words, the theme of this book is debatable. That is why several top contributors, rather than a single pre-eminent author, were needed to portray for the public both the present state of knowledge and views as to the possibilities that lie before us. Such exposure of diversity is essential for public understanding of the nature of scientific inquiry as a basis for judgments involving human action. Nothing could be more unlike science than to set forth the views of any one scientist as holy gospel beyond criticism and reasonable disagreement. Statements of eminent scientists are heeded because they are likely to be based on wide and deep knowledge and cogent reasoning, but they are examined critically nevertheless.

An enlightened public, it is hoped, will go through the same processes of critical appraisal and judgment that scientists expect of each other.

In view of the diversity of present opinion, the recency of acquisition of the knowledge on which many of the opinions are based, and the accelerating speed of acquisition of new knowledge, it is a fair question to ask whether the facts and views and problems dealt with in this book are ephemeral and likely to be out-of-date very soon. It is, of course, always hazardous to express an opinion about the future course of scientific progress and how it will affect earlier knowledge and views. There is no reason at present to doubt, and every indication to believe, that both general and human genetics will continue to progress with great rapidity and that this progress will include some at-present-unpredictable sensational breakthroughs. Such advances may be expected to add significantly to the knowledge portrayed in this book as current, may modify or replace some of it, and may even provide new and presently unforeseen ways of controlling the direction of human heredity and evolution.

However, it is difficult to imagine that any advances would significantly alter the basic problems with which this book deals. At least for centuries hence, barring total annihilation, the problem of man's control of his own heredity and evolution will become increasingly demanding of attention. The details of knowledge and of ways and means will of course change, but the basic problem with its ethical, moral, religious, and political overtones will persist. Because this book's main objective is to arouse public awareness of the present existence of the problem, of its firm foundation in rapidly growing knowledge, and of the increasing need for intelligent and wise public judgments and actions in regard to it, this book should not become rapidly outdated, like so much current and definitely dated popular science, but should retain an important and continuously current valuable function for a very long time.

The Contributors

Professor Salvador Luria was educated in Italy for the medical profession. He came to the United States in 1940 and worked successively at Columbia, Vanderbilt, Princeton, Indiana, and Illinois before going to the Massachusetts Institute of Technology in 1959. His influence on modern biology has been tremendous. He was one of a few leaders who created modern virology and viral genetics. His widely known and richly appreciated researches have been matched by his great success as a teacher. Among his many successful students, the most distinguished, James Dewey Watson, shared the Nobel Prize for a contribution that is the keystone of the revolutionary new biology.

Dr. Edward Tatum went to the Rockefeller Institute in 1957 after having served at Wisconsin, Stanford, and Yale. Like Luria, he too has had a Nobel Laureate student, Joshua Lederberg, a giant of microbial genetics. Tatum, together with Beadle, created modern biochemical genetics, which led the way to our current understanding of what genes do at the molecular level. This knowledge—along with the discovery of what genes are and of several remarkable genetic happenings in microbes—is the basis for present speculations about control of the direction of human heredity. Moreover, Tatum led the way toward considering application of the new genetics to man. In the speech he gave on receipt of the Nobel Prize in 1958, he pointed out how the new genetic knowledge someday might be used medically to counteract hereditary defects. To him, perhaps more than to any other one person, the train of events that has led to this book may be traced.

Dr. KIMBALL ATWOOD, like Dr. Luria, holds an M.D. degree which he obtained at New York University. After interning at Bellevue Hospital, he worked at Columbia University, Oak Ridge National Laboratory, and the University of Chicago before becoming Chairman of the Microbiology Department at the University of Illinois. His highly original researches have been divided with equal fruitfulness between the genetics of man and the genetics of the bread mold, *Neurospora,* made famous by Tatum and Beadle.

Dr. ROLLIN HOTCHKISS was trained as an organic chemist but later brought his chemical knowledge to bear on genetic problems. He has served on the faculty at Yale and as a visiting investigator at the Massachusetts Institute of Technology and at the Carlsberg Laboratory in Copenhagen, Denmark, but most of his scientific work has been done at the Rockefeller Institute in New York, where he has been on the staff since 1935. His outstanding contributions to bacteriology won him the Commercial Solvents Award of the American Society of Bacteriologists. He has long been and continues to be one of the few leading investigators of bacterial transformation, the nature and importance of which are discussed throughout this book.

Dr. ROBERT DEMARS, the youngest of the contributors, began his studies under the tutelage of Dr. Luria at Indiana University and went with him to the University of Illinois, where he completed his work for the Ph.D. After a year as postdoctoral fellow at the California Institute of Technology, he joined the faculty of Washington University for three years and the National Institutes of Health for two years, before taking his present position in the Department of Medical Genetics at the University of Wisconsin five years ago. Like most of the other leading workers on human cell genetics, he entered that field after considerable experience in microbial genetics.

Dr. GUIDO PONTECORVO, like Dr. DeMars, came to human cell culture work after experience with general and microbial genetics. Born and educated in Italy, he was trained later in fruit fly and general genetics in Edinburgh, Scotland, under the tutelage of Dr. H. J. Muller. After the hard times of the war, during which he was isolated in Britain as an enemy (Italian) alien—perhaps not entirely a misfortune because it gave him leisure to study and think—Pontecorvo entered the new and lively field of genetics of lower organisms, choosing to work with certain queer fungi, which a lesser man might have shunned because of their oddities that seemed to present insuperable difficulties for genetic study. Pontecorvo brilliantly turned these difficulties into unique opportunities and thereby revealed some amazing genetic mechanisms. A Fellow of the Royal Society of London, he holds the Chair of Genetics in the University, Glasgow, Scotland.

Dr. WACLAW SZYBALSKI was trained in chemical engineering in Poland where he received his D.Sc. degree at the Institute of Technology in Danzig in 1949. The following year he was Visiting Professor at the Institute of Technology in Copenhagen. In 1951 he came to the United States and remained four years on the staff of the Biological Laboratory at Cold Spring Harbor, Long Island, N.Y. Then, after five years at the Institute of Microbiology at Rutgers, he went four years ago to the McArdle Memorial Laboratory of the University of Wisconsin. Dr. Szybalski, like Drs. DeMars and Pontecorvo, went into the field of genetics of mammalian cell cultures after experience with the genetics of microorganisms. His current studies on the possible extension of bacterial transformation to mammalian cells comprise one of the most provocative discoveries bearing on the possibility of applying to man important discoveries made originally on microorganisms.

Dr. GEORGE KLEIN was born in Budapest, Hungary, but emigrated to Sweden where he is head of the Institute for Tumor Biology of the Stockholm Karolinska Institute. He has made a great reputation by his remarkable studies of the steps by which normal mammalian cells become malignant tumor cells. In the course of this work he always has had in the forefront of attention the genetic bases of these changes and also the changing immunological antagonisms between host and graft. The fields of his special competence figure importantly in evaluating the practicability of some proposals for extending knowledge of microbes to man.

Dr. H. J. MULLER is widely recognized as one of the most eminent biologists of his generation. He was one of the famous small group that laid the foundations of genetics at Columbia University in the decade following 1909. He then went to Texas, first at the Rice Institution and then at the University of Texas. There he made the epoch-making discovery in 1927 that the rate of occurrence of mutations can be enormously increased by exposure to x-rays, a discovery for which he won the Nobel Prize. Muller's pioneering, imaginative researches in genetics were continued for relatively short periods in Moscow, Berlin, Edinburgh, and Amherst before he settled at Indiana University in 1945, where he has been since 1953 Distinguished Service Professor of Zoology. A leading humanist, Muller has long been deeply concerned with a great variety of human problems, to the resolution of which he has brought unsurpassed knowledge, imagination, and fervor.

The convener of the symposium and editor of the book, T. M. SONNEBORN, had the good fortune of entering the field of genetics of microorganisms long before it became popular, under the influence of H. S.

Jennings, the father of this field, at Johns Hopkins University. Sonneborn's researches have dealt mainly with the genetics of a unicellular animal, *Paramecium,* in which he has discovered a number of the mechanisms by which the genes, the rest of the cell, and the environment interact in cellular heredity and development. After serving at Johns Hopkins until 1939, he moved to Indiana University, where he has been since 1953 Distinguished Service Professor of Zoology.

Acknowledgments

This book is the edited record of a symposium held on April 6, 1963, at Ohio Wesleyan University, Delaware, Ohio, as part of the ceremonies dedicating a new life sciences building, Bigelow-Rice Hall. When Dr. Robert Long asked me to organize a symposium for that purpose, I agreed to do so on two conditions: that the subject would be control of the direction of human heredity and evolution, and that I could succeed in obtaining nothing less than top-flight participants. For encouraging a symposium on so controversial and "dangerous" a subject and for every possible cooperation in bringing it to fulfillment, we—and we believe the public—are deeply indebted to President Elden T. Smith and Vice President W. Noel Johnston of Ohio Wesleyan. Dr. Elwood Shirling, as local Program Chairman, was of inestimable help in many ways. Dr. William F. Hahnert, General Chairman, and Dr. W. D. Stull, as Chairman of the Committee on Arrangements, made our short visit to Delaware a most pleasant one.

Ohio Wesleyan and we are grateful to the National Science Foundation for the financial support essential for so ambitious an undertaking. The Foundation's Program Director for Genetic Biology, Dr. Herman Lewis, is to be credited with the vision that recognized the potential importance of our design and with presenting it successfully to the Foundation for support.

Finally, the value of the symposium and the book is obviously attributable to the speakers and the discussants. Their expertise, imaginative foresight, thoughtful concern for man, and enthusiasm to take pains to lay before the public facts and possibilities of deep and far-reaching importance made the symposium and the book outstanding contributions to public information on problems that will in the future demand increasingly the formation of wise public judgments. The editor takes credit only for formulating the design, selecting the participants, persuading them to undertake the labor in the midst of their busy lives, and editing (subject to the approval of the participants) the tape recording of the discussion.

T. M. Sonneborn

Contents

PART I

The Nature of the Revolutionary New Biology

CHAPTER 1

Directed Genetic Change: Perspectives from Molecular Genetics

S. E. Luria, Department of Biology
Massachusetts Institute of Technology

Molecular Genetics—a Key to Biological Progress

If knowledge is power, the science of genetics has placed in the hands of man an impressive amount of power in the last few decades. Sixty years ago, the subject of heredity and variation was the *hic sunt leones* of biology textbooks. In succession, genetics discovered the genes as discrete, durable, material units of heredity; their location and linear assembly in the chromosomes of the cell nucleus; the random, sporadic, but essentially orderly processes by which genes and chromosomes change; the nature of the relationship between the genes and the hereditary traits they determine; and even the chemical nature of the genes themselves, the chemical mechanism of their replication, and the chemical nature of the messages they dispatch. Finally, the very language of the gene has been deciphered: the three chemical alphabets–of the gene, of its messages, and of its products–have been understood in their main features and are rapidly being decoded. Molecular biology has played the role of comparative linguistics; bacteria and viruses, genetically the most accessible of organisms, have provided the Rosetta stone for these momentous advances.

The triumphs of molecular genetics–I shall return to them in more detail later—have enriched biology tremendously. Despite some ill-advised claims that all basic problems have been solved, and some equally ill-advised warnings that the molecular approach ignores the more unique aspects of life, it is clear that molecular genetics has cleared the way for effective approaches to the more complex problems of biology. How do the cellular and organismic patterns arise in which the messages of the genes are to be expressed? How are certain patterns selected, others rejected, both in development and in evolution? How are controls exerted, from the external environment and from within the organism, on the function and structure of the genes? To draw on an archeological analogy, we may think of the genes as encoding the laws of a civilization. Deciphering the alphabet and grammar of the legal code, and even the law-proclaiming machinery, does not in itself reveal or describe a civilization. Yet, it provides the most powerful approach to understanding the conceptual framework of the culture, hence the structure and operation of the civilization.

But biology is not only a pure science searching for explanations of the phenomena of life. It also has immediate concerns with practical application. The power stemming from the knowledge of molecular genetics is certain to be used in medicine, agriculture, and animal husbandry—the classical fields of applied genetics. The topic of this book concerns still another field of applied biology: the possible control of human heredity. The prospect, whether welcome or unwelcome, of purposefully directing human heredity has always centered in eugenics: the selective increase or decrease of certain hereditary constitutions both by selective reproduction and by selective restraint on reproduction (1). A new question is now raised: does the new knowledge of the genetic material and of its function open the door for a more direct attack on human heredity?

The Responsibility of Biologists. Before I discuss the prospects as I see them, let me consider briefly the question of values (2). I have already stated that biology is not, strictly speaking, a pure science. In fact, almost no science is completely pure since its findings always bear, however indirectly, on human affairs. The impact of a science on human affairs imposes on its practitioners an inescapable responsibility. This responsibility actually affects the course of scientific development: on the one hand, it creates the urge to seek useful applications and to foster their general acceptance; on the other hand, it may restrain the scientist from pursuing a line of research that is clearly leading to evil applications. The instance of nuclear fission research is a natural illustration of the many moral alternatives that face the natural scientist in his work.

Science creates power. The uses to which this power will be put in human affairs involve choices and decisions, that is, value judgments. It would be as improper for scientists to claim the right to decide alone—that is, to advocate technocracy—as to abdicate their right and duty to make themselves heard in the decision-making process. This implies a special responsibility of scientists: that of informing the public of the actual and potential applications of their findings and of the possible consequences.

Yet, the progress of science is often so rapid, almost catastrophic, that it creates an imbalance between the power it places in the hands of man and the social conditions in which this power is exerted. Then, neither warnings of scientists, nor breadth of public information, nor wisdom of citizens may compensate for inadequacies of the institutional framework to cope with new situations. For example, the major problem facing the world today is the disparity between the power of modern weapons and the effectiveness of the machinery for settling international problems. Using a biological concept, we might say that imbalance stems from a lack of preadaptation of society to the new environment created by the advances of physical science. By science and technology, human society forges stupendous tools for its own progress; but, like the inexperienced sorcerer, it comes at times dangerously close to being drowned by the sudden flood of power it has unleashed.

I submit, therefore, that the scientist has an additional, more subtle responsibility. Like a pilot who keeps an eye on his instruments, charting the future course of his vessel, the scientist should cultivate his own alertness to prospective scientific developments that may suddenly add new powers to man. And he should, within the limited means at his disposal, prepare the public to cope with the foreseeable consequences of advances he anticipates.

Let me cite a case history. Natural radioactivity—the transmutation of elements—was discovered early in this century. Rutherford produced artificial transmutation in 1919. The neutron was discovered in 1932. By 1934, artificial radioactivity was a reality. Nuclear fission, accomplished in 1935, was not interpreted as such until 1939, although the notion that nuclear bombardment might lead to tremendous and utilizable energy release had been considered by physicists for several years. The chain reaction concept, and its awesome applications, followed rapidly. The point is that physicists could and did realize the nature and magnitude of the power they were manipulating, even though they questioned the chances of harnessing it. When this power became reality, society was unprepared, both intellectually and institutionally, to deal with it. Would a different course have been possible? I doubt it; yet probably most thoughtful physicists would agree that they could have done more to anticipate the almost inevitable developments of nuclear physics and to inform society of the impending challenge. Perhaps the scientific habits of skepticism and restraint, of curbing fantasy and distrusting fancy, inhibit the scientists' effort to speculate on what the future may bring.

My reason for raising these issues is my conviction that the problem of directed change of human heredity, if ever solved, will raise basic issues of human values and public policy; and that although genetics today does not afford ready means to change human heredity directly in specific ways, it permits and indeed forces us to consider as possible certain advances that would place within the power of geneticists the capability of doing exactly that.

The rest of this paper will present the grounds for this opinion. My discussion will be based only on considerations of molecular genetics derived from work on bacteria and viruses. I shall conveniently ignore the tremendous problems of biological engineering that will have to be solved before a direct attack on the human germ plasm is accomplished. I have two reasons for doing so: first, these problems, while extremely difficult in practice, are probably not such in principle; second, their discussion (fortunately for me) has been assigned to other contributors to this book.

Structure of the Genetic Material

Nucleic Acids and the Genetic Code. The central generalization of modern genetics is that all hereditary "know-how" *at the molecular level* is embodied in nucleic acids. (I italicize the words *at the molecular level,* to remind the reader of an important qualification. Since every cell comes from another cell, the pattern of cellular organization itself has hereditary characteristics. We have no operational ways to test whether all hereditary patterns of organization are gene-derived unless we learn to create a cell by gene action; for a discussion of this problem, see Sonneborn [3]).

Nucleic acids are prototypes of "language substances." To a repetitive backbone made of a chain of sugar molecules and phosphate groups joined together there are attached at equal intervals certain substances—called purines and pyrimidines—chosen from a very restricted variety. These molecules "code" the nucleic acids, in the same way that certain symbols impressed at equal intervals on the tape of a computer code a program onto it (4). There are two types of nucleic acid: DNA (deoxyribonucleic acid), whose coding symbols are (mainly) the four substances adenine, guanine, thymine, and cytosine (A, G, T, and C); and RNA (ribonucleic acid), whose symbols are adenine, guanine, uracil, and cytosine (A, G, U, and C). By weak but precise chemical bonds, substance A pairs specifically with substance T (or U); G pairs with C.

In ultraschematic form, the present tenets of molecular genetics are as follows (5): The chromosomal genes consist of DNA. The DNA in chromosomes is double-stranded: any sequence (for example, AACATGC) on one strand is matched by and paired with the complementary sequence (TTGTACG) on the other strand. DNA replicates; that is, it is copied by a specific catalyst, which from appropriate building blocks assembles a new complementary tape along each of the pre-existing ones. In this way, one double tape generates two double tapes (see Figure 1). One gene gives rise to two genes at each cell generation (6).

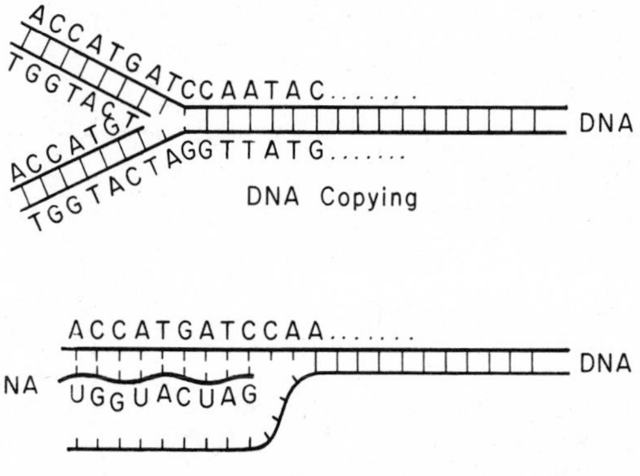

FIGURE 1. Copying of DNA and its transcription into message RNA. The solid straight lines are the sugar-phosphate backbones of DNA, held together by hydrogen bonds (the cross-lines). The wavy line is the sugar-phosphate backbone of RNA.

DNA also generates RNA transcripts: a DNA code sequence is transliterated into a complementary RNA sequence by a special catalyst (Figure 1). For example, AACATGC generates UUGUACG (7). These RNA tapes are the messages that convey from the genes to the body of the cell the instructions for making proteins, which are the chemical machine tools of the cell. The instructions in the RNA message are translated into protein language: a sequence of three RNA symbols (a three-letter word) provides the code for one constituent of protein–one of 20 molecules, called amino acids, which we may symbolize as *a, b, c, d, e*. . . . For example, UUG may code for *d,* UGA for *m,* and so forth. Thus the nucleic acid language, written in a four-letter alphabet, is translated into the language of the proteins with its 20-letter alphabet. The translating machinery appears to be relatively simple. It consists of a set of catalysts and of a corresponding set of large molecules acting as carriers (these carrier molecules are themselves made of a special kind of nucleic acid). Each of the 20 amino acids (*a, b, c*. . .) is hooked by its own specific catalyst to its own carrier. These carriers then "read" the RNA message; that is, they line up along it according to the code, and the amino acids are then zipped

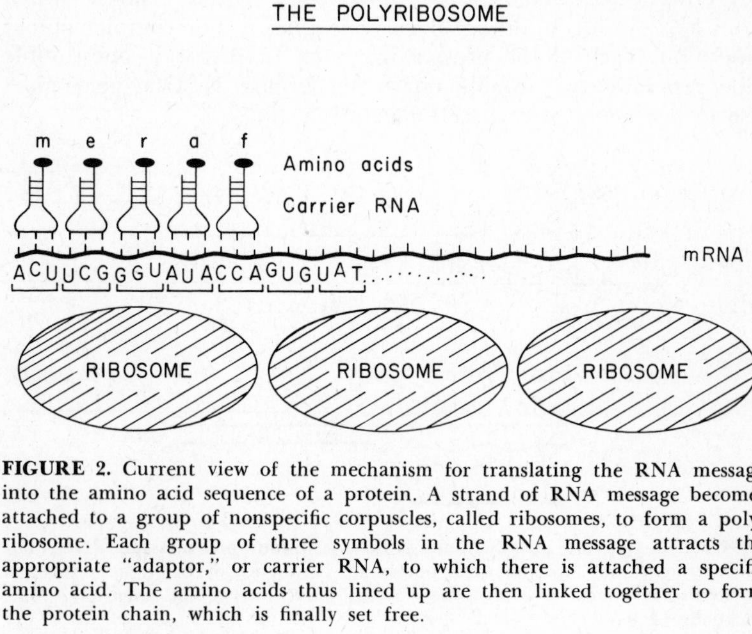

FIGURE 2. Current view of the mechanism for translating the RNA message into the amino acid sequence of a protein. A strand of RNA message becomes attached to a group of nonspecific corpuscles, called ribosomes, to form a polyribosome. Each group of three symbols in the RNA message attracts the appropriate "adaptor," or carrier RNA, to which there is attached a specific amino acid. The amino acids thus lined up are then linked together to form the protein chain, which is finally set free.

together into a protein chain by a special zip-up catalyst (Figure 2). Note that this translation mechanism is strictly a one-way process: there is no translating machine in the direction of protein to nucleic acid. Proteins are neither copied nor translated. They just work (8).

What, then, is a gene? It is a certain stretch of DNA, which has the code for a given protein (9). A protein chain of, say, 100 amino acids is coded by a DNA stretch of 300 symbols. A small bacterium has about 1 mm of DNA tape, enough to code about 10,000 different protein chains. The smallest virus has enough DNA for about four or five; a human cell, enough DNA for 1 million different proteins.

At least in some bacteria and viruses, we have good reasons to believe that the whole DNA of a cell may form a single linear structure, that is, a single tape one molecule thick (10). In fact, there is no indication of any discontinuity in the DNA: no breaks, no joints, no specially weak points in the backbone. It is at least permissible to view the genetic material of such an organism as a single, continuous, gigantic double tape of DNA, an infinitely monotonous chemical landscape into which is inscribed, however, the enormously varied and exciting code of the laws of the cell. Even for large cells like those of man, with their 46 chromosomes and their enormous load of DNA, it is not excluded that each chromosome may contain a single continuous giant DNA fiber a foot long or more (11).

But, of course, the apparent monotony of the genetic landscape is deceiving. Not only must each gene be different from all other genes in its coded message, but it must also in some way be marked off from the other genes. In fact, when genes generate their messages, they do so as units, not in continuous chains. Each message is a relatively short piece of RNA, the transcription of a gene or of a small group of genes, not of the whole DNA tape. Therefore, the transliterating mechanisms must know where a gene begins and where it ends. And it appears that, as in any other language, the transcription of each gene into an RNA message occurs in one direction only, say, always from left to right (12).

Also, not all genes work all the time. In fact, most genes are idle most of the time. For example, in the cells of the liver the genes that make digestive catalysts work very actively, but the genes that make substances specifically needed for cell division may not work at all for years and years, as long as the liver cells are not dividing. Yet these genes are still there. Let a large portion of the liver be removed surgically from a rat, and within a few days most of the remaining cells begin to divide. In a week or so they have replaced the lost portion (13). Now, at least in bacteria, we know fairly well how the switching on and off of genes is done. There are certain genes whose task is to regulate other genes. The products of these regulatory genes can block or "repress" specifically the function of other genes by combining with certain genetic regions, the so-called "operator regions" (14). Thus, the repressor substances must know how to recognize the genes they repress (Figure 3).

What the "starting points" and the "operator regions" of the genes are we do not yet know. Maybe the starting point is a special sequence of code symbols (for example, 13 A's in a row). Maybe it is a bit of another substance attached to or inserted in the DNA. Maybe it is a chemical singularity in DNA itself. In fact, what I said earlier about the monotonous composition of DNA, with its unending sequence of A's, G's, T's, and C's, is not quite true. There are in DNA some minor components, that is, some few molecules chemically related to A, T, G, or C, which are occasionally interspersed among the common symbols. It is conceivable that these minor components of DNA are related to the signals where DNA starts or stops being copied or transcribed (15).

So much for the structure and function of the DNA genes. Before turning next to the question of the accessibility of genes to specific attack, I would like to introduce two other topics: accessory genetic elements and RNA genes.

Accessory Genetic Elements. The traditional view has been that the amount of genetic material in all cells of an organism and of all organisms of a species is constant (apart from deletions or reduplications of small genetic segments). All cells of an animal such as man have the same genetic complement. Losses or reduplications of chromosomes, when they occur, cause serious malformations and often are lethal. A number of findings in microbial genetics have raised, however, certain interesting questions regarding the quantitative variability of the gene complement. There exist, in bacteria as well as in protozoa, a variety of accessory, dispensable genetic elements, which can enter cells from outside and replicate within them, and can be lost or eliminated without damage to the cells. In bacteria at least, some of these accessory genetic elements can even join up physically with the main gene string and exchange genes with it. Elements of this type have been called episomes (16).

Another line of evidence bearing on the same point comes from the study of virus action. This has made it clear that viruses are simply devices by which certain bits of genetic material work their way from the cells of one host to those of another (17). Sometimes the entrance of these migrant pieces of genetic material that we call viruses destroys the host cells. But in many cases the viral genes remain in a cell without killing it, replicate when the cell genes replicate, and, like episomes, can even become attached more or less permanently to the cellular chromosomes. This is true of the viruses that attack bacteria (the bacteriophages) and may be true also of viruses that attack man. The genes of these persistent viruses can function in the cells of their hosts and may be responsible for permanent cellular changes, including some leading to cancer. Also, some of these viruses can, at least in bacteria, incorporate into their own structure some of the genes of the host. When they invade other hosts, they can transfer to the chromosomes of the new hosts the genes they have appropriated. This process is called transduction.

Thus, the genetic material of a cell, and of an organism, is not necessarily fixed in amount. Hence it may be possible to bring about changes not only of quality but also of quantity. It may be feasible to add or to subtract from the gene complement of an organism if it already contains or if it can accept some accessory dispensable portions.

RNA Genes. There has been much discussion as to whether cells have RNA genes in addition to DNA genes. Most evidence for the existence of RNA genes is somewhat questionable, except for the existence of viruses that contain RNA and no DNA. That the RNA is the genetic material of these viruses cannot be doubted. One can produce chemical changes directly in the RNA of a virus and produce mutants (18). This is especially clear with some viruses whose RNA can be extracted, purified, treated with mutagenic substances, and then used directly to infect new cells. The progeny virus derived from the treated RNA contains many mutants. How does the RNA of these viruses replicate in the host cells? The evidence indicates that it is actually copied, without intervention of DNA, by special enzymes, which apparently are manufactured under the direction of the virus itself. Since we have no reason to suspect that the RNA of viruses differs substantially from other RNA, it is reasonable to keep open the question of whether cells do possess RNA genes, whose mechanism of replication has for some reason not yet been discovered. This question must remain unanswered at present, but it should be kept in mind as we proceed to the next part of our discussion, namely, how can we change the genetic material?

Perspectives for Selective Genetic Changes

Induced mutations, whether of the localized type, that is, the change or removal of one or more code units in a gene, or of the organizational type, that is, transfers of portions of genetic material from one position to another, always have had an exquisitely random quality. The agents that can produce mutations–radiation, chemicals, high temperatures–act at random on the genetic material. They work by increasing the frequency of most mutations, not by singling out specific genes and changing them (19). The randomness is, of course, the direct consequence of the chemical monotony of the genetic landscape. This lack of selectivity is present also for some more subtle mutagens that attack specifically one or another of the four code symbols of DNA, either changing them or substituting themselves in their place when new DNA is made. Even these mutagens can select only among the four symbol molecules, each of which is present in hundreds or thousands of copies within each gene.

If directed genetic change is to be accomplished, that is, if the goal is to change or remove the specific gene, much greater selectivity is required. What kind of process can provide it?

Removal, Addition, and Replacement of Genes. Let me deal first with some of the most obvious although not necessarily most feasible approaches. Certain bacteria, as I already mentioned, possess accessory genetic elements, some of which can be transferred from cell to cell by contact (16). Chemicals are known, including some dyes, that can specifically remove these elements by blocking their replication. Genetic elements of this sort are also well known in protozoa, and in fact much of our present knowledge of extranuclear heredity is based on the elegant studies by Sonneborn and his colleagues on extranuclear genetic elements in some paramecia (20). If accessory elements of this kind were proved to be present in human cells and to play a role in determining genetic traits, one might attempt to introduce them, remove them, or exchange them. For this approach, as well as for other approaches of this kind, peculiar techniques using cells cultivated outside the body would be required; this problem I shall leave to other authors in this book.

Next, viruses may be invoked. One might find in man, as in some bacteria, viruses that under certain conditions produce permanent changes of cells without damaging them. One might then even expect that such viruses, once introduced in the human body, may find their own way to the cells of the germ plasm. This seems hardly a likely prospect at present, but with viruses one can never tell. In some fruit flies, for example, there is a virus-like agent that makes the flies easily killed by carbon dioxide. This agent, after entering a fly, finds its way to the cells of genital organs and so gains access to the next generation of flies. Removal of the agent can be accomplished, thereby curing the flies of their excessive sensitivity to carbon dioxide (21). Some such phenomenon might turn up in man.

Or, we might invoke transduction. As I have already mentioned, some viruses of bacteria occasionally join up with the cell genes and incorporate some of them in place of their own. Likewise, viruses might be found in man that can transfer genes from cells of one individual to those of another.

Finally, bacterial genetics suggests another and more likely possibility—transformation. In several types of bacteria, one can extract fragments of DNA large enough to retain their functional integrity and yet small enough to penetrate, under suitable conditions, into intact cells. If these recipient cells differ by one or more genetic traits from those that have donated the DNA, some of the recipients are transformed, that is, they acquire some of the traits of the donor (22). In fact, the donor DNA seems to have a hard time entering the bacterium, but once entered, it is remarkably efficient in replacing the corresponding resident piece of DNA. This ability of the DNA of one gene to single out, pair with, and replace its homologous DNA among the hundreds or thousands of DNA segments present in a cell is one of the most surprising qualities of nucleic acids. In bacteria, the process of transformation is both inefficient and unselective, because an extract of a cell contains a mixture of all its genes. The inefficiency may be obviated to some extent by improved methods of treating the recipient cells; the lack of selectivity, by the concentration and purification of DNA fractions corresponding to specific genes. Some progress, although very little as yet, is being made in this direction.

We may push speculation even a little further. If the code sequence of a given gene can be deciphered, it might then be feasible to synthesize in vitro a segment of DNA with a desired, "improved" sequence, but with enough similarity to the recognized sequence of the gene in question to be able to replace it in the genetic apparatus. The prospects for deciphering the sequences of specific genes will be discussed again below. As for the applicability of the transformation process to human cells, we have some ground for anticipating positive results. It has already been possible to infect human cells in culture with the pure nucleic acid of certain viruses (23). Also, attempts to transform human cells using DNA extracted from other cells have given some positive results. These findings are discussed in other parts of this book.

Selective Changes in Gene Structure. We can now return to the problem of inducing specific changes in the structure of specific genes. Assume at first that no special singularities are recognizable in the genetic landscape aside from the code sequence itself. We ask then: How specific does an agent have to be in order to single out a given gene? Or, more correctly, how much information must a mutagen contain in order to recognize the specific sequence of code symbols of a given gene? The answer is, of course, an amount comparable to that of the gene itself. For example, for a DNA segment 1000 links long we may need a mutagen that can read 1000 symbols or, at least, the shortest unique sequence of symbols present in that segment (for instance, 100). Hence, any specific mutagen must be a long molecule. But what kind of molecule? One that can read, that is, selectively combine with, the substance of the gene in such a way as to change it, either directly or by altering its replication. First, we must look at some natural products.

1. The RNA transcript of a gene is the most precise analogue of that gene one can ask for. This transcript or message RNA can actually be isolated by selectively combining it with the strands of its model DNA (24). In this way, it has been possible to separate the RNA transcript of a few specific genes of bacteria and of viruses (25). Any general applicability of this method is far from being in sight. But the present results already suggest some exciting prospects. On the one hand, it may be possible to learn the actual sequence of chemical symbols in a given gene without having to isolate that gene in a pure state, by isolating its RNA transcript and reading its chemical code sequence. One could then try to prepare some chemical with the proper affinity for that sequence, so that it combines with the gene. Alternatively, one might use the transcript RNA itself as a tool, by so treating and modifying it that, when replaced into a cell, it will act as a mutagen by attacking its own gene or by interfering with its replication.

2. Another natural source of gene-specific mutagens might be the regulatory substances, mostly repressors, which by combining with the operator regions of the genes control and regulate their function (26). The nature of the repressors is still unsettled, but the isolation and identification of some repressors may well have been accomplished by the time these lines are printed. Such substances, with their specific affinity for certain genes, might provide unique starting points for making specific mutagens by shrewd chemical manipulations.

3. Still remote, but not inconceivable, is the production of anti-

bodies directed against a given gene. Antibodies are a class of blood proteins that are formed in animals in response to injection of foreign substances and can then combine specifically with these substances. The antibodies are large molecules, which contain enough structural information to tell apart other large molecules otherwise very similar to one another. Although generally the "recognizing" faculty of antibodies is limited to relatively short molecular spans, it is conceivable that antibodies against specific genes, or against their RNA transcripts, might be prepared. Until now antibodies against specific DNA have been produced only with some peculiar types of DNA isolated from certain viruses (27). Yet, this approach is being pursued, and its future developments may be of great interest to molecular geneticists.

Singularities in the Genetic Landscape. It has already been mentioned that some peculiar "minority" letters occur in the otherwise monotonous four-letter alphabet of the DNA. Their function is still unknown. If these minority symbols are located at random and are functionally interchangeable with their counterparts, then they do not provide any sites for selective attack. If, however, they should prove to be located at strategic points, they might be a suitable target for specific mutagens.

We already know, from work on viruses, that within a gene a few sites are exceptionally mutable, often 100 times more than the other sites (see Figure 3)—the so-called "hot spots" of spontaneous or induced mutation (28). Whatever the nature of these spots may be—special minority letters, or, more probably, special sequences of letters particularly prone to change—they indicate that exceptional vulnerability of some portions of genes by otherwise nonspecific mutagens is within the realm of possibility. If one knew what the hot spots were, one might try to reach them by specific means.

There is a second type of singularity to be considered—one in fact that is a property of every gene. This is the timing of its replication. At least in bacteria (but I would guess also in other organisms) the genes do not replicate all at the same time or at random times, but in sequence. In bacteria one wave of replication starts from one end of the single gene string and reaches the opposite end before a new wave of replication begins (29). In synchronized populations of bacteria, therefore, all copies of a given gene, a billion or more in a culture, are being replicated at the same time. Clearly, this permits us to envisage a new method for selective attack. If one of those mutagens that can act on DNA only at the time it is being copied was administered to a synchronized cell population for a very short time, it could produce mutations only on the one gene that was being duplicated at that moment. By changing the time of treatment, one might produce mutations in specific genes at will. Again, we are still far from applying this

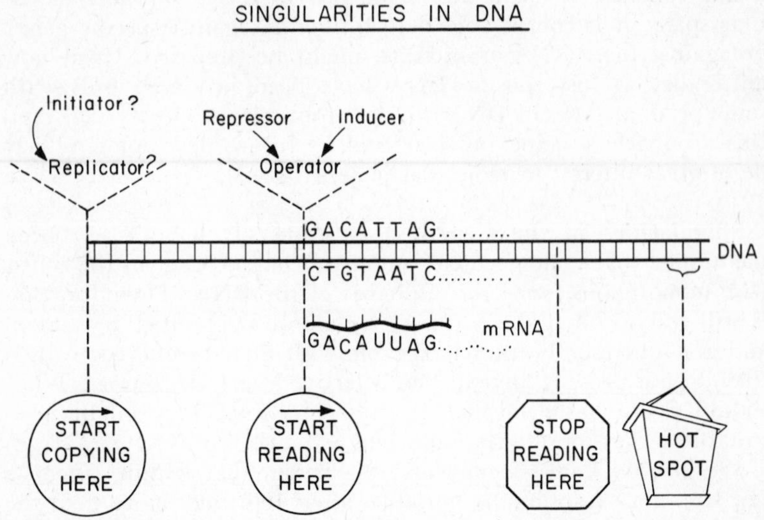

FIGURE 3. Some special regions in DNA. The point where DNA starts being copied is the *replicator,* which must be acted upon by the *initiator.* The points where transcription of RNA messages begins are called *operators* and are the sites of action of the *repressors* (counteracted by *inducers*). Exceptionally mutable sites are called *hot spots.* The nature of replicators, operators, and hot spots (as well as the end points for transcription) is still unknown.

approach in practice, let alone applying it to human heredity. But the feasibility of this approach, at least in bacteria, seems very promising.

Actually, we can go a step further and ask: What causes a string of genetic material to start replication? What signals tell where and when to start? In cells of animals and plants the replication of DNA, when it occurs, occupies only a small part of the cycle of cell division. Clearly, some signal must be provided. In bacteria and viruses, it has been suggested that each genetic string, chromosome or accessory element, may have a starting point for reduplication, a "replicator," whose function is activated by an "initiator" produced elsewhere in the cell (30). The replicator-initiator system would be analogous to the operator-repressor system already mentioned in the discussion of gene function (see Figure 3). By interference with a replicator-initiator system, it may be possible to alter selectively the reproduction of certain parts of the genetic apparatus.

Summary

The gist of this discussion can be summarized in a few paragraphs. From the standpoint of molecular biology we see today no clear and open paths to directed control of human heredity or, for that matter, of any heredity except possibly bacterial. Even at this level, the powerful tools of genetic change still suffer from a substantial limitation—numerical inefficiency. For example, by transformation with DNA one can change 1 or maybe 10 per cent of the treated cells but not 100 per cent. Nor can one change a specific cell with 100 per cent efficiency. Only in some virus infections can one approach the degree of efficiency of directed change that would be a prerequisite for any constructive application to human genetics. Yet, inefficiency is not in principle an insurmountable obstacle. Biological engineering can probably overcome it by manipulating and selecting directedly changed cells, possibly germ cells or their precursors, and by using them as carriers of the changed heredity. The required advances in technology may not be conceptually greater than those that were needed to convert nuclear fission from a laboratory experiment to a self-sustained chain reaction.

It must also be noted that the inefficiency of the methods that might be used to bring about selected gene changes may hinder the development of planned, orderly applications to human heredity for agreed purposes of improvement, but may not constitute a major obstacle to the use of such methods for evil purposes of human degradation or subjugation.

As for foreseeable developments that may radically alter the picture, three main possibilities should be considered: (1) the role of accessory genetic elements in human heredity, (2) the existence of specific singularities in the linear structure of genetic materials, and (3) the synthetic creation of selective mutagens of high informational content, the natural substances with specific affinity for genes—their primary products and their regulators—being used as models, and possibly as starting materials.

The first of these possibilities depends on new discoveries in human genetics. In this area, molecular genetics as studied in bacteria and viruses can be of use only in suggesting model systems and analogies. The second and third possibilities are those in which molecular genetics is directly involved. In these areas we realize how deeply the recent advances of molecular genetics have affected biological science.

The real impact of molecular biology is not, as misplaced emphasis would sometimes have it, in the prospect of explaining all phenomena of life in terms of chemistry and physics. Life as the selective maintenance and adaptive evolution of complex patterns of organization will retain its uniqueness as a phenomenon—and biology its uniqueness as a science—no matter how many biological processes we learn to translate into terms of physical mechanisms. Rather, the real contribution of molecular biology is that, by revealing the chemical languages in which the biological order is embodied at various levels of the functional organization of cells, it has provided novel and precise means of intervening directly at those levels, not only to understand and explain, but to modify and possibly also to create.

To return to my initial subject, does the present status of genetics confront the geneticist with any new responsibility? I would say that nothing at present would justify either the prediction of a coming millennium of human betterment or the proclamation of an impending danger of genetic enslavement. Geneticists are not ready to conquer the earth, either for good or for evil.

Neither should we shut our eyes, however, to the possibility that within a few years some powerful means to control directly the heredity of man, as well as of other organisms, will have been forged by work already in progress. Fifty years ago, such a prospect would probably not have unduly worried our grandfathers. The culture of enlightenment had fostered in them the comfortable conviction that human progress and the ideals of human brotherhood were advancing monotonously at a steady, if often uneven, pace. But such Pollyannaish beliefs were proved naïve and premature by the events of the last half-century—the shattering by World War I of the illusion that international disputes inevitably would be resolved by statesmanship; the rejection of the ideals of human worth by Nazi Germany; and the gradual acceptance of total war against unarmed human beings in World War II. No longer can we believe that the growth of knowledge and control over our physical environment will itself guarantee that the resulting power will be utilized wisely. Neither need we, however, subside into fatalistic despair or withdraw into the ivory tower of social agnosticism. What we, in anticipation of the remarkable advances that may soon be forthcoming, can do is to attempt to create some machinery by which the social implications of our work can be debated rationally and openly so that any important decision as to its applications will be arrived at by an informed and well-advised public. I would not think it premature, for example, for the United Nations as well as the National Academy of Sciences of the United States to establish committees on the genetic direction of human heredity. It is a good beginning that we in this book have started earnestly to debate these problems.

References and Footnotes

1. See *Daedalus,* **90** (3) : Summer 1961 (especially article by H. J. Muller, p. 432).
2. For an enlightening discussion of this topic, see J. Bronowski, *Science and Human Values.* Harper and Bros., New York, 1959.
3. Chap. 14 in *Genetics in the 20th Century* (L. C. Dunn, ed.). Macmillan, New York, 1951; *Proc. Nat. Acad. Sci. U.S.A.,* **46**:149, 1960; and chap. 7 in *The Nature of Biological Diversity* (J. M. Allen, ed.). McGraw-Hill, New York, 1963.
4. J. D. Watson and F. H. C. Crick, *Cold Spring Harbor Symposia Quant. Biol.,* **18**:23, 1953; *Nature,* **171**:737, 1958.
5. These concepts are of necessity presented here in a dogmatic form. The reader is referred to original articles quoted below for more cautious presentation.
6. A. Kornberg, *Science,* **131**:1503, 1960. Elegant analyses of the mode of replication of DNA in living cells have been performed by M. Meselson and F. Stahl, *Proc. Nat. Acad. Sci. U.S.A.,* **44**:671, 1958, and by J. H. Taylor, P. S. Woods, and W. T. Hughes, *ibid.,* **43**:122, 1957.
7. A detailed discussion of the transcription mechanism is given by E. Volkin in *Molecular Genetics* (J. H. Taylor, ed.), Vol. 1, p. 271. Academic Press, New York, 1963.
8. See F. H. C. Crick, in: *Progress in Nucleic Acid Research* (J. N. Davidson and W. E. Cohn, eds.). Academic Press, New York, 1963. An early forceful presentation of the ideas underlying current developments was given by the same author in *Sympos. Soc. Exp. Biol.,* **12**:138, 1958.
9. Some genes have regulatory functions, controlling the activity of other genes. Whether or not these regulatory genes give rise to proteins is not known (see ref. 13).
10. See J. Cairns, *J. Molec. Biol.,* 3:756, 1962, and C. A. Thomas, Jr., in: *Molecular Genetics* (J. H. Taylor, ed.), Vol. 1, p. 113, 1963.

11. Other interpretations are considered by J. H. Taylor, in *Molecular Genetics,* Vol. 1, p. 96, 1963.
12. The elegant experimental evidence was published by F. H. C. Crick, L. Barnett, S. Brenner, and S. J. Watts-Tobin in *Nature,* **192**:1227, 1961, and summarized by Crick in *Sci. Amer.,* p. 66, October, 1962.
13. See A. D. Glinos, in: *The Chemical Basis of Development* (W. D. McElroy and B. Glass, eds.), p. 813. Johns Hopkins Press, Baltimore, 1958.
14. See F. Jacob and J. Monod, *J. Molec. Biol.,* **3**:318, 1961, and *Cold Spring Harbor Symposia Quant. Biol.,* **26**:193, 1961.
15. D. B. Dunn and J. D. Smith, *4th Intern. Congress Biochem.,* **7**:72, Vienna, 1958.
16. F. Jacob, P. Schaeffer, and E. L. Wollman, *Sympos. Soc. Gen. Microbiol.,* **10**:67, 1960.
17. This viewpoint has been presented in detail by A. Lwoff, *J. Gen. Microbiol.,* **17**:239, 1957, and by S. E. Luria, *Science,* **136**:685, 1962, and *Cancer Res.,* **20**:677, 1960.
18. See A. Tsugita and H. Fraenkel-Conrat, in: *Molecular Genetics* (J. H. Taylor, ed.), Vol. 1, p. 477. Academic Press, New York, 1963.
19. After the initial discovery of the mutagenic effect of radiation by H. J. Muller, (*Science,* **66**:382, 1927), many physical and chemical treatments have been shown to be mutagenic. For a discussion of their mode of action at the molecular level, see E. Freese, in: *Molecular Genetics* (J. H. Taylor, ed.), Vol. 1, p. 207. Academic Press, New York, 1963.
20. See T. M. Sonneborn, *Advances Virus Res.,* **6**:229, 1959. Note also that in plant cells the chloroplasts, that is, the corpuscles that contain chlorophyll and perform photosynthesis, have a semi-independent type of heredity (M. M. Rhoades, *Cold Spring Harbor Symposia Quant. Biol.,* **11**:202, 1946). Recently it has been suggested that chloroplasts contain some DNA, different from that of the cell nucleus (E. H. L. Chun, M. H. Vaughan, and A. Rich, *J. Molec. Biol.,* **7**:130, 1963).
21. Ph. L'Héritier, *Advances Virus Res.,* **5**:195, 1958.
22. Proof that bacterial transformation was due to transfer of DNA was obtained by O. Avery, C. M. McLeod, and C. McCarty (*J. Exp. Med.,* **79**:137, 1944). This was a major landmark in molecular biology, proving the genetic role of DNA. The current status of bacterial transformation has been reviewed by A. Ravin, *Advances Genet.,* **10**:61, 1961.
23. See J. S. Colter and K. A. O. Ellern, *Ann. Rev. Microbiol.,* **15**:219, 1961.
24. B. D. Hall and S. Spiegelman, *Proc. Nat. Acad. Sci. U.S.A.,* **47**:137, 1961; E. K. F. Bautz and B. D. Hall, *ibid.,* **48**:400, 1962.
25. For a few bacterial genes, this has been done using the DNA of transducing phages, which contain some of the host gene, as a trapping agent to capture the RNA messages corresponding to these genes (see

G. Attardi, S. Naono, F. Gros, S. Brenner, and F. Jacob, *C. R. Acad. Sci. (Paris)*, **255**:2303, 1962, and M. H. Hayashi, S. Spiegelman, N. C. Franklin, and S. E. Luria, *Proc. Nat. Acad. Sci. U.S.A.*, **49**:729, 1963.

26. See ref. 13 and chapter by E. L. Tatum in this volume.
27. L. Levine, W. T. Murakami, H. Van Vunakis, and L. Grossman, *Proc. Nat. Acad. Sci. U.S.A.*, **46**:1038, 1960.
28. A clear discussion is presented by S. Benzer in *Sci. Amer.*, p. 70, January 1962. A technical presentation by the same author is in *Proc. Nat. Acad. Sci. U.S.A.*, **45**:1607, 1960, and **47**:403, 1961.
29. H. Yoshikawa and N. Sueoka, *Proc. Nat. Acad. Sci. U.S.A.*, **49**:806, 1963.
30. S. Brenner and F. Jacob, *C. R. Acad. Sci. (Paris)*, **256**:298, 1963.

CHAPTER 2

Perspectives from Physiological Genetics

Edward L. Tatum
The Rockefeller Institute

The primary purpose of this book is to evaluate possibilities of applying basic concepts, principles, and techniques of molecular biology and genetics to the heredity and evolution of man. In so doing we first will be confining our attention to the technical and experimental possibilities, avoiding immediate consideration of the important philosophical, moral, and ethical problems with which society will be faced as to the use to which any successful experimental techniques should be put. The technical and experimental possibilities have emerged primarily from two developments: the intensive and fruitful investigation of eminently suitable experimental materials, microorganisms and viruses; and the investigation—mainly in these materials—of the nature, structure, and functioning of genetic material, hand in hand with the development of powerful new biochemical and biophysical methods. It may be helpful to introduce our subject by commenting briefly on each of these.

What particular attributes of microorganisms have made their experimental genetic manipulation possible and profitable? One important attribute is that the most-used microorganisms normally have only one gene of each kind or at least have this condition during a major part of their life cycle. In technical terms they are haploid, in contrast to the body cells of most higher organisms, which are diploid, that is, have two genes of each kind. Therefore, in microorganisms each gene expresses itself immediately and simply. On the contrary, in diploid organisms some genes (called recessives) may remain hidden and unexpressed when the other gene of that kind is dominant.

Two other important attributes of microorganisms are their small size and rapid growth and reproduction. These attributes make it possible to deal readily with large populations of individual cells in a minimum of space. This, in turn, permits finding and evaluating any population changes, even very rare ones such as mutations of a particular type, in a statistically valid manner. The experimenter can start with a single cell or entity, rapidly obtain from it a large homogeneous population of descendants, and expose the population to a variety of chemical, physical, and biological agents and conditions to produce mutations. He can then apply to the population very rigorous selective procedures with reasonable expectation of isolating, and quickly raising again to a large population, very rare mutant cells or units. Similarly, he can obtain, isolate, and multiply types arising not by mutation but by other events such as recombinations of the genes of two kinds of cells or units, even when the recombinants are exceedingly rare, occurring in less than one cell or unit in a million.

The haploid state, the astronomically large numbers of obtainable individuals, and the facility with which rare mutations and recombinants can be obtained, found, and isolated have made it possible to demonstrate the existence in microorganisms of several different mechanisms of transfer of genetic information (forms of genetic recombination) and to improve the efficiency of these processes by selection of appropriate strains and by improvement of facilitating conditions. The consequent availability of several different and experimentally effective modes of genetic recombination in microorganisms has in turn added another dimension to their utility to the molecular biologist. In later chapters, Drs. DeMars and Pontecorvo discuss the extent to which mammalian cell cultures are analogous to microbial cultures in regard to the attributes just outlined.

Successful study of the genetic material at the molecular level has played a decisive part in the emergence of the technical and experimental possibilities we are to consider. This area is now known as molecular genetics (1, 2) or, more broadly, molecular biology. Since Dr. Luria set forth its main features in the preceding chapter, we need restate briefly for orientation little more than the four principal relevant concepts. (1) The genetic material is now believed to be DNA or, in exceptional instances, RNA. (2) The storing of information in DNA, or/and RNA, is now generally believed to be in terms of a nonoverlapping triplet code of base sequences in the nucleic acid molecule. (3) The stored information is replicated by unidirectional assembly of new DNA strands complementary in base sequence to those serving as templates. (4) The information coded into DNA is transcribed via RNA by a mechanism that results in the translation of each specific DNA base triplet into a specified amino acid in the final polypeptide product, the protein or enzyme.

With these concepts, gene mutation in its simplest form is viewed as the substitution of one base in a triplet by another as a consequence of faulty replication, or in more complex forms as the deletion of one or more bases or the addition of extra bases. Finally, the outlined concepts, as elaborated, extended, and refined in studies principally with microorganisms, permit the molecular biologist to view the broad outlines of some of the mechanisms by means of which gene expression is controlled in an orderly fashion, as in processes of cellular differentiation and embryonic development.

We would seem to be justified in concluding that there is no reason to suspect the principles of coding, reading, and regulation of genetic information to be essentially different in microbes and in man.

Similarly, there seems some basis for optimism in believing that any successes in manipulating or controlling the genetic material of microorganisms should eventually be applicable to higher multicellular organisms, including man. In later chapters, Drs. DeMars and Pontecorvo take up the theoretical and practical possibilities of such developments. In preparing the stage for them, I shall try to evaluate biological engineering in microbes, first, as to the present state of the art and, second, as to possibilities of improving such manipulations in specificity, directivity, and efficiency.

Biological engineering seems to fall naturally into three primary categories of means to modify organisms. These are:

1. The recombination of existing genes, or eugenics.
2. The production of new genes by a process of directed mutation, or genetic engineering.
3. Modification or control of gene expression or, to adopt Lederberg's (3) suggested terminology, euphenic engineering.

Let us consider first eugenics, or the recombination of existing genes. This means bringing different genes, existing in different cells or individuals, together in the same cell or individual, thus in effect creating a new combination of hereditary traits. In microorganisms, there are two main types of procedures, differing in gross mechanism, by which genes (DNA) are transferred and subsequently recombined.

1. Procedures involving the coming together of two cells. Of these, three types can be distinguished. First, the conjugation process in bacteria involves the coming together of two bacteria with transfer of part or all of the chromosome of one into the other (4). Second, in certain haploid but multinucleate fungi that lack complete subdivision into separate cells, parts of two individuals fuse into one. This results in bringing their diverse nuclei into a common cytoplasm. The resulting individual, because it possesses diverse nuclei (Gr. *Karyon*), is said to be heterocaryotic. Occasionally these diverse nuclei fuse, forming diploid nuclei which later may return to the haploid condition with new combinations of the chromosomes from the two original nuclei. This complex sequence of processes, discovered and used so brilliantly by Pontecorvo and his associates (5), resembles in essence sexuality and is referred to as parasexuality. Third, in both bacteria and certain fungi, reduction to the haploid condition after fertilization is occasionally incomplete, leaving the organism with an extra part of the chromosomal material over and above the haploid amount. In these cases, the parts present twice may later reduce to a single dose, again with recombination.

2. Procedures involving the transfer, without contact of entire cells or organisms, of only single genes or a small group of closely linked genes. Of these, two types are very important in bacteria. First, DNA molecules alone, i.e., the genic material, from one kind of bacterium may enter another bacterium and become incorporated by recombination into the gene-set of the recipient bacterium. This process is known as *transformation* (6). Second, a virus living in one bacterium may carry genes (i.e., DNA) of the bacterium with it when it leaves its host and enters another bacterium. In the latter, the genes thus brought in may likewise become incorporated by recombination into the gene-set of the recipient bacterium. This process is known as transduction (7).

It is probably superfluous to point out that the transduction process may be viewed as transformation by the process of virus infection. The elucidation of this process, and of the role of DNA in transformation, played equally vital roles in the development of the basic concepts of molecular genetics.

In considering the possibilities of improving the specificity, directivity, and efficiency of these types of microbial eugenics, let us take up each in turn.

Experimental recombination at the cellular level in bacteria has improved strikingly in efficiency since its discovery in 1946, partly as a consequence of increased knowledge of physiological conditions conducive to conjugation, but even more as a consequence of the selection of more fertile stocks (4). At first the frequency of conjugation, estimated from the frequency of recombinant cells, was calculated to be one in about a hundred million bacteria; following the discovery of more fertile (Hfr or high frequency of recombination) stocks, the frequency of conjugation under ideal conditions now approaches 100 per cent efficiency with a corresponding increase in recombination frequency. Further knowledge that fertility in bacteria is based on sexually compatible types, characterized by F^+ (male) and F^- (female) factors, has permitted the detection and improvement of recombinational potentialities in stocks of bacteria that had originally been thought to be infertile. As far as efficiency of "eugenic" recombination by conjugation in bacteria is concerned, there is little room for further improvement with the best stocks now known, although the less fertile cultures and species can be considerably improved.

With elucidation of the process of physical transfer of the linear bacterial chromosome during conjugation in Hfr stocks, the possibility of controlled transfer of specific genes became experimentally practical. This followed from several discoveries. First, during mating the linear chromosome of the male (F^+) enters the female starting at a definite point, so that the gene at this point enters first. Second, means were discovered to stop the mating at any time, making it possible to introduce into the female (F^-) only the one or few genes near the starting point. Third, the starting point itself differs in different stocks of bacteria, so that different stocks can be used to inject different genes (located at different points on the chromosome) into a female. Actually, the bacterial chromosome before mating appears to be circular and to break during mating at a definite point (the point that enters first), this breakage point differing in different stocks. The breakage point is apparently determined by the position occupied by a factor, the Hfr factor, characteristic of Hfr stocks referred to above; and this factor is located at different points on the circular chromosome in different stocks. Improvement in the specificity and directivity of gene transfer at conjugation thus becomes possible by improving the control, by mechanical or chemical means, of initiating and terminating the linear transfer of the bacterial chromosome during conjugation, and by selecting donor Hfr stocks that have the Hfr factor located close to the particular gene to be transferred.

In view of the inherent differences between bacterial and mammalian cells, particularly the existence in the latter of a discrete membrane-bounded nucleus containing two sets of chromosomes instead of only one, there seem to be only limited opportunities of extension to these cells of improved microbial techniques of intercellular recombination. One possibility might be the selection of mutant cells with increased potentialities for cell fusion, or the discovery of environmental conditions more favorable to this. The binucleate cells thus formed might then (hopefully) undergo nuclear fusion and reduction, with gene recombination, as in the fungal parasexual process. The formation of binucleate cells or heterocaryons might be complicated by cellular incompatibility and injury as a consequence of genetic differences. If this problem were not involved or could be obviated, heterocaryons conceivably could be produced, not only by cell fusion, but also by nuclear transplantation. Granting the remote possibility of separation of different chromosomes of a chromosome set by physical or chemical methods, or their identification by direct observation, microinjection methods might even be used for establishing specific "partly heterochromosomal" cells, with some improvement in specificity of gene transfer and recombination.

Let us now proceed to a consideration of bacterial recombination by transformation (6). As with cell conjugation, the efficiency and reproducibility of transformation in the laboratory have been considerably improved since its discovery. This resulted largely from increasingly detailed knowledge of the environmental and physiological conditions affecting cell receptivity to the transforming DNA, "competence" to incorporate this DNA into the bacterial gene-set, and improved knowledge or better methods of handling DNA so that its vital informational activity is retained. Potentiality for further significant improvements in specificity and therefore also in efficiency seems to be greater for transformation than for mechanisms of cellular recombination. This possibility rests primarily on the feasibility of obtaining pure single DNA "species," or genes, either by isolation or by synthesis. Methods are now being developed that should, perhaps in the near future, permit the isolation of a single desired DNA gene. These methods use nucleic acids from suitable mutants and select the desired part of the nucleic acid by exploiting the specific union of a given DNA with its exactly complementary RNA. Once enough molecules of an individual DNA species are available, their quantitative amplification by enzymatic reactions easily can be foreseen. It is already known that the enzyme DNA polymerase catalyzes the synthesis of whatever DNA is used as a primer. The practicality of this method is evidenced by the recently reported in vitro replication of biologically effective transforming DNA obtained from the pneumonia bacterium, *Diplococcus pneumoniae*.

Alternatively, or supplementarily, methods for complete analysis of the base sequence of RNA, and hence at least deductively of its complementary DNA, can be expected to be developed and applied in the near future. With knowledge of the base sequence of a desired DNA, the next step will be the chemical or enzymatic synthesis of this molecule. It has been established already that only one molecule of DNA need be transferred to effect the transformation of a single genetic unit, and that most types and species of DNA compete for entrance into a recipient cell. Hence the theoretical possibilities of improving specificity and efficiency via single DNA species-transformation would increase with the degree of purity of the transforming preparation of DNA; since there are 1000 to 10,000 species of DNA in a bacterium, absolute purity could improve specificity and efficiency 1000- to 10,000-fold.

It is too soon to speculate on the possibility of transformation by RNA instead of DNA, although suggestive results have been reported both with animal cells and with bacteria. If this proves a reality, it could carry exciting possibilities for the future, since it would appear that the synthesis of a desired RNA species may prove simpler and sooner attainable than that of a desired DNA species.

In respect to either RNA or DNA, we should mention the even more speculative possibility of the direct chemical synthesis of a desired sequence of bases as deduced from knowledge both of the amino acid sequence needed for a particular protein, and of the genetic code specifying that sequence. This goal well may be closer than we realize. Perhaps, even, with more detailed understanding of what parts of the structure of proteins are involved in enzymatic activity and how they so function, nature may be improved upon by the genetic engineers of the future by their making more or differently active enzymes. This area might be termed neogenetic engineering.

The preceding possibilities of increasing the efficiency and specificity of transformation of bacteria would seem to apply equally to cells of all other kinds. However, the difficulties are compounded in diploid cells, when the two genes of a kind are initially both dominant and it is desired to transform to the recessive trait.

Practical considerations therefore would seem to restrict applications of transformation in diploid organisms to possibilities of transforming haploid germ cells, or somatic cells induced first to undergo reduction division, or of transforming recessive to dominant genes. Fortunately, many or most mammalian traits needing rectification by genetic engineering are indeed recessive. Hemophilia, phenylketonuria, alkaptonuria, and albinism are a few well-known examples (8).

We will now discuss transduction, its limitations and potentialities (7). There seem to be several possibilities in this mechanism for increased efficiency and specificity of gene transfer and subsequent recombination. One is the selection of specially useful natural or induced mutant strains of virus. Ideally, one could increase specificity and efficiency of infection, decrease host cell injury, and thus increase transducing efficiency by suitable and imaginative selection methods. The finding of a transducing virus P1 that crosses species boundaries and the isolation of viruses that distinguish F^+ and F^- bacterial cells are examples that encourage optimism. Perhaps equally encouraging is the hope of significantly increasing the specificity of transduction by the use of different viruses that specifically transduce different genes. Bacterial viruses tend strongly to transduce the genes adjacent to the site in the chromosome where the virus is normally attached, and different viruses have different favored or absolute sites of chromosomal attachment. For example, the virus lambda is attached to the bacterial chromosome at or near the locus of the gene for galactose fermentation and it transduces the galactose gene exclusively. In addition, if the virus picks up the gene during replication and if the gene is incorporated into the chromosome of the recipient cell also during replication, as appears reasonable, then some improvement in efficiency and specificity of transduction might conceivably be anticipated by using both as donors and recipients synchronously dividing cells at appropriate stages of replication, for the bacterial chromosome and the attached virus are replicated synchronously, presumably starting at one end of the chromosome.

A related type of transduction, with even greater specificity of gene transfer, is illustrated by the F factor (4). The sex or fertility factor F belongs to a peculiar class of genetic factors called episomes, which also appear to include some that determine resistance to drugs or antibiotics. Episomes are associated only transitorily with the chromosome. When they dissociate from the chromosome, they may carry with them an adjacent gene of the bacterial chromosome.

The episome and the gene then replicate together as a single unit and do so even when the bacterial chromosome is not replicating. This results in multiple copies of the episome and gene in each cell. Hence, when conjugation occurs, the episome-gene combination has a high probability of rapid transfer to the recipient cell. By stopping conjugation mechanically very soon after it begins, one can transfer just the one gene carried with the episome. The episome F, when it has no gene attached, can attach anywhere in the bacterial chromosome and so pick up any gene. But, when it has a gene attached, it regularly attaches only at the position of that gene. Using this information, therefore, it is possible to develop strains that are pure for F and any particular gene and that therefore transmit any desired gene and only that gene to recipient cells. Such transfer by the F factor is called sex-duction or F-duction; in general, genic transfer by episomes may be called "episome-duction."

The possibilities for the use of transduction or episome-duction in genetic engineering of cells other than bacteria are largely unexplored, but certainly would appear promising. The same limitations would apply here, however, as discussed for transformation, especially dominance relations. Nevertheless it has already been suggested that episomes may be involved in regulation of developmental processes of higher organisms, and that the action of viruses in bringing about "transformation" of normal mammalian cells in culture into cancer cells bears at least superficial and formal similarities to bacterial transduction.

It would appear that none of the techniques of microbial genetic engineering has sufficient efficiency or specificity to warrant much hope of its eugenic applicability to more than an exceptional situation in developing or fully developed intact higher organisms such as man. The possibilities would seem considerably more favorable, or perhaps favorable only, when applied to cell populations under culture outside the body. These can be treated, manipulated, and subjected to the necessary ruthless and biologically wasteful selective procedures. One should not, however, overlook the possibility that some new methods of transfer of genetic information not analogous to microbial methods, and peculiar to mammalian body cells, may be found. Nor should one deprecate the utility of even rare instances in man that may well prove amenable to microbial techniques.

We now come to the second main topic, directed gene mutation, or "genetic engineering." Since Dr. Luria has already discussed this area in detail, I will add only a few speculative possibilities.

These could involve the mutational treatment of DNA in various forms: in intact cells, in nuclei, or as isolated chromosomes; in potentially transducing viruses; in episomes; or as isolated DNA. Cells containing or acquiring the treated DNA would then be screened by rigorous selective methods to isolate the desired mutant cell. With animal cells, this genetic engineering would be incomplete without ways of extending the induced genetic change from the cell level to that of the whole organism. The problems involved in this would seem to be precisely the same for cells resulting from directed mutation as for cells derived by recombination.

I would like now to consider a few possibilities of increasing the specificity and directivity of induced mutations, even at the risk of further infringement on Dr. Luria's topic. One may conceptually distinguish between specificity as controlled by nature of the mutagenic molecule or agent, and that in which the effectiveness of the mutagenic agent is modified or controlled by environmental conditions.

In the first group the most promising possibility for the future would seem to be the development of chemical mutagens in which a reactive group is attached to a carrier molecule with specific affinity for certain chromosomal regions. Potential candidates for such specific carrier molecules might be: synthetic or natural nucleotides or polynucleotides including messenger RNA; actinomycins or their derivatives which attach specifically to areas of DNA rich in guanine residues; base analogues; and antibodies to protein-conjugated purines or pyrimidines which have been shown to cross-react strongly with single-stranded DNA. Conversely, molecules that bind specifically to DNA might protect the binding sites from the action of separately applied mutagens, either chemical or physical.

In the second group, among the conditions that might be effective in increasing directivity of mutagens, several might be suggested as potentially fruitful.

1. Critical stages during replication, or during RNA production. Stages during which genes are specially sensitive to induced mutation probably exist. These stages might be fixed in time by synchronous division or by differential gene activity as controlled by gene repression or induction.

2. Particular internal or external cell environments. These may favor stabilization or loss of unstable, transitory states of DNA occurring in the process of inducing mutations by mutagens.

3. The addition of DNA-specific molecules, such as repressors,

messengers, and antibiotics (actinomycin). These may affect the incorporation of base analogues into replicating DNA.

4. Addition of antibodies against nucleic acid bases, the purines or pyrimidines. Because they bind specifically to single-stranded DNA, such antibodies would be expected to act on DNA during replication when the two strands are separating.

Finally, we come to the third general area of biological engineering, "euphenic engineering." This area would be defined, in contrast to "eugenic" and "genetic" engineering, as the control and regulation of phenotype rather than of genotype. Expressed in different terms, euphenic engineering in microbes would encompass all conceivable methods of controlling gene expression without changing the genes themselves. In a multicellular organism such as man, euphenic engineering would also include any modification of gene expression that would not involve hereditary changes.

Although euphenic engineering is not formally pertinent to the subject of this book, since it does not per se involve heredity and evolution, several considerations appear to me to justify its brief inclusion.

First, the presentation and understanding of the concepts of molecular biology would seem incomplete and one-sided without inclusion of our related concepts of the regulation and control of gene action at the level of phenotype.

Second, it can be proposed that insofar as successful euphenic engineering would prevent or correct the expression of detrimental genes and thus permit the survival of otherwise biologically unsuccessful individuals, it would add to the diversity of the gene-pool of the race available for the processes of mutation, recombination, and selection involved in evolution.

Third, and perhaps most immediately pertinent to this book, euphenic engineering would seem to be the first step in the development of methods and techniques of applying either "eugenic" or "genetic" engineering to man. As will be discussed shortly, it would seem most feasible to apply the techniques of these two classes of biological engineering first to human body cells in culture. Their reimplantation into an individual might then be considered euphenic engineering since the reintroduced body cells would not participate in reproductive or evolutionary processes, but might modify the phenotype of the individual.

A logical and reasonable progression of development of capabilities in biological engineering in man would seem to be from euphenic engineering on body cells, to their reimplantation, and finally to the application of "eugenic" and "genetic" engineering techniques to the germ cell lines.

In considering the potentialities of euphenic engineering, it is reassuring that the developmental biologist is coming to attribute more and more significance, in the complex process of differentiation and development, to differential activation and nongenetic control of gene function.

It is also reassuring to realize that, with increasing knowledge of the details of the long and complicated sequence of chemical events involved in the translation of gene structure into protein structure (1), more and more steps in this sequence are becoming accessible to willful manipulation and purposeful control.

Let us follow this sequence through some of its complexities. We must point out first of all that each step in it is in itself almost certainly subject to genic control in some degree. For example, the functioning of "structural" genes, which are responsible for the ultimate structure and therefore the quality of proteins, is controlled by "regulator" genes. These "regulator" genes, the best-understood examples of which are microbial "operator" and "modifier" genes, affect the quantitative expression of the structural genes. Such genic control is not so direct or simple in some other steps from gene to protein. There is also a "gray zone" in which genic and environmental control factors interact in the production of proteins, particularly enzymes, as the following examples show.

Studies with microbes have clearly established the phenomena of enzyme repression and inhibition, and their significance in regulatory processes (2). An end product of metabolism, when present in sufficient concentrations, may block further functioning of an enzyme critically involved in the formation of that end product. This has been termed "feedback enzyme inhibition." In this case it would appear that the action of the gene responsible for making the enzyme is not being inhibited, but that the inhibition is operating at the level of activity of enzyme on its substrate. In other instances, however, it has been shown that the end product actually "represses" production of the enzyme. A priori, this repression could be at any level between the formation of genic "messenger" RNA and the final step in the synthesis of the enzymatic protein. However, demonstration of coordinate repression of the functions of several closely linked genes favors the assumption that repression functions at the gene level. Moreover, in a limited number of instances it would appear that the activities of genes within a certain segment of the chromosome, an operon, are controlled by an adjacent gene, the "operator." The functioning of this is in turn controlled by "repressor" or "inducer" molecules, which may be metabolic end products, substrate molecules or products of a specific "regulator" gene that interact with the small molecules. According to this hypothesis, the actions of inducer or repressor would be their regulation of the synthesis, on a DNA template, of "messenger" RNA. The action of the repressor would appear to be analogous to, but more specific than, the inhibition of DNA-dependent RNA synthesis by binding of actinomycin to DNA. Complexity, and therefore flexibility, of control can also be illustrated by the phenomenon of "multivalent" repression, in which several species of end products cooperate in regulating the production of an enzyme involved in a reaction common to several biosynthetic sequences.

Another illustrative example of the "gray zone" mentioned earlier, and of another point of control of protein synthesis, concerns "suppressor" genes. In contrast to the regulator genes just discussed, suppressor genes affect quality rather than quantity of the ultimate product of a structural gene. There is experimental evidence that certain suppressor genes correct the placement of an "erroneous" amino acid in a mutant protein which has been due to a mutation of one of the "code words" (DNA base triplets) in a gene. The attractive hypothesis has been suggested that they do so by changing the specificity of a particular sRNA molecule. Since each kind of sRNA molecule is specific for a particular amino acid, and is responsible for carrying it to the correct position on the RNA template in the ribosome, an appropriate change in sRNA could make it specific for carrying a different amino acid. Thus, at the level of translation in the ribosome, such a change in an sRNA could correct for the original error in a mutant DNA base triplet. A related type of control could occur in cases of so-called "degeneracy," i.e., the existence of two or more code triplets and, correspondingly, of the same number of sRNA species, for the same amino acid. A mutant change in one sRNA, which made it specific for a different amino acid, then would not necessarily be lethal or harmful. Thus, the existence of two or more sRNA species for the same amino acid might permit some selection of the proteins into which a mutant DNA would cause an amino acid replacement.

I cannot resist interjecting here my protests at the adoption of the cryptographers' designation of *degenerate* for *alternate* code symbols. The biological meaning of degeneracy is completely at odds with the cryptographic meaning. From the biological point of view, the acquisition of alternate code symbols for an amino acid, with its potentialities for adaptability in the control of protein synthesis, would seem an evolutionarily advantageous development, rather than a degeneracy.

To resume, it would seem obvious from this discussion that gene action can be modified at a number of different levels by environmental factors. Any of these should be susceptible points of attack in euphenic engineering, through the utilization of feedback inhibition and repression.

In contrast to the somewhat speculative aspects of progress in those directions, it is surprising, and gratifying, that the simplest form of euphenic engineering is already standard human therapy. This is the limitation of the production of an undesirable metabolite by dietary restriction of substrate, as in phenylketonuria or galactosemia. Obviously, any means of modifying reaction rates, via repression, enzyme inhibition or competition, or cofactor limitation or inhibition, would be equally effective.

It might also be pointed out that replacement of a missing or defective gene-product also constitutes euphenic engineering. Examples include particular substances readily carried in the blood, or normal blood constituents, such as gamma-globulin, antihemophilia proteins, hormones, or, perhaps in the future, needed enzymes.

Promising possibilities for future developments in such engineering would seem to be: the modification of the induction-repression gene regulatory system by nonmetabolizable analogues of the normal compounds; modification of a faulty translation process by the administration of appropriate sRNA fractions, either synthetic or isolated; and the use of natural regulators or analogues thereof, perhaps such as hormones.

One of the principal foreseeable limitations to the effective application to man of the various suggested techniques of euphenic engineering would seem to be the need for continued therapy throughout life. Another limitation would be their restriction to the use of readily available agents or materials with stability and solubility properties suitable for administration orally or by injection, and readily available to and utilizable by the target cells, tissues, or organ systems. There is room for optimism that both of these limitations may be bypassed or obviated by the use of cells, or perhaps only a certain fraction of those cells, from the organ or tissue in which the genetic defect is primarily expressed. If this is granted, any of the three types of biological engineering might then be applied usefully to human cells in culture provided that an effective number of the appropriately modified cells could be reimplanted into the organism successfully.

There would seem to be three general possibilities of overcoming the immunological barriers that would limit successful implantation of cells. Recombinants might be selected not only for the desired character involved but also for cell compatibility. More optimistically, cells of the particular individual candidate for therapy could be isolated, cultured, converted, selected, and reimplanted. Finally, it may be feasible, with further understanding of the mechanisms involved in immunological responses and tolerance, to remove this limitation. Thus, if the immunological restriction could be removed, corrective biological engineering could then be carried out by the transplantation of naturally occurring genetically desirable cells, tissues, or even organs, from another individual.

In conclusion, I would hesitate to make a prediction as to when and to what degree the principles and techniques of the "newer genetics" will be successfully applied to man. However, I believe that this will come, and perhaps sooner than we suspect, with the breaking of a few major barriers. Before biological engineering is an accomplishment of the present rather than a possibility of the future, we must find time and energy to devote to the even more difficult question of how this knowledge can best be used for the welfare of all mankind. Perhaps we should begin to think seriously about this even now and to plan for the future in anticipation, rather than in retrospect, and possibly too late.

References

1. C. B. Anfinsen, *The Molecular Basis of Evolution.* John Wiley & Sons, New York, 1959.
2. R. P. Wagner and H. K. Mitchell, *Genetics and Metabolism,* 2nd ed. John Wiley & Sons, New York, 1964.
3. J. Lederberg, Molecular biology, eugenics and euphenics. *Nature,* **198**:428-29, 1963.
4. F. Jacob and E. L. Wollman, *Sexuality and the Genetics of Bacteria.* Academic Press, New York, 1961.
5. G. Pontecorvo, The parasexual cycle in fungi. *Ann. Rev. Microbiol.,* **10**:393-400, 1956.
6. R. D. Hotchkiss and E. Weiss, Transformed bacteria. *Sci. Amer.,* **195**:48-53, 1956.
7. N. D. Zinder, Transduction in bacteria. *Sci. Amer.,* **199**:38-43, 1958.
8. H. Harris, *Human Biochemical Genetics.* Cambridge University Press, Cambridge, England, 1959.

Discussion—Part I

Dr. Atwood

Very little can be added to the complete description and prospectus presented by Drs. Luria and Tatum. However, I would like to comment on some of the things they have discussed, such as the technical feasibility of control of heredity beyond that which is possible simply by selective breeding. Now, in the sense that similar objectives might be accomplished, it is difficult to draw the line between control by selective breeding and the direct manipulations mentioned. One main difference between them is that selective breeding is technically feasible, whereas at present most other means of influencing heredity are not. There may be some instances, however, in which this situation is reversed. Control of sex ratio is such an example. Although not very important in itself, it seems to show that there are some eminently feasible controls not yet referred to, and to illustrate that some of these may soon come to pass.

There has been much publicity about control of sex ratio in the past, but no actual success. Yet it seems now that spermatazoa containing X and Y chromosomes may be separated by means, for example, of density gradient centrifugation. This problem is being attacked very actively in certain laboratories because of its economic importance in animal breeding where more animals of one sex or the other are needed. It is not inconceivable that the same service may be offered to human beings. This seems rather trivial to wish for and also rather harmless, but there may be other opinions on this.

More important is an instance in which we already have the separate pieces that, when put together, would constitute an actual use of DNA transformation in medicine. There is a disease called orotic aciduria, which, fortunately or unfortunately depending on your viewpoint, is extremely rare. Persons with this disease are unable to synthesize for themselves two of the bases that are essential ingredients of nucleic acid, but they get enough of these in the diet. Now if they lose their appetite, as children do when they are sick, the dietary intake falls below that necessary to keep up the production of new cells, which requires of course that nucleic acid be synthesized. So the blood count may drop to disastrous levels. Now, animal experiments have shown that a very small number of marrow cells would be capable of repopulating a bone marrow that has been depleted of its blood-forming cells, e.g., by radiation. So, if we could provide a very small number of normal cells as a starting inoculum for an individual with orotic aciduria whose blood count has become low, he might repopulate his bone marrow with normal cells because of the extremely strong selection for these cells when food intake is subnormal. The procedure of choice would be to remove some of the patient's own bone marrow cells, to subject them to the Szybalski mammalian cell transformation technique using normal DNA, to return them to the individual, and then temporarily to adjust the diet to favor overgrowth by any normal cells (perhaps a single one would be sufficient) that could synthesize their own nucleic acid. This would effect a euphenic cure of the disease. Now of course this would not have much impact on public health, as only two cases of orotic aciduria are known! But it gives some idea of what might be done if conditions were right.

Another thing that has been done in animals and doubtless could be done in man is the induction of parthenogenetic development. In rabbits the ovum has been caused to develop without fertilization by cooling it at the right moment during its passage down the oviduct. In such cases both sets of chromosomes come from the mother, for there is no father. The individuals so produced, although all female, are not exact replicas of their mother; they represent different combinations of her two sets of genes.

Incidentally, there is a widely circulated story about this. An endocrinologist wanted to try this on a human female. So, he obtained as a volunteer an unmarried woman from Boston. But the theological school at Harvard caught wind of these developments and decided that he ought to be advised to desist. After hearing this story and believing it for years, I talked to this endocrinologist who told me that it was absolutely not true. In any case, this sort of thing surely *could* be done.

A cell nucleus transplanted to an ovum can give normal development of an individual genetically identical with the nucleus donor, as shown in amphibia by Briggs and King. In principle, this should work in mammals, and would be a means of multiplying an otherwise unique individual.

Now I would like to comment further on some possible consequences of really complete technical mastery. Of course, complete mastery includes not just knowing how to create specified sequences of DNA, but also knowing just what they will do in the context of the developing organism and the rest of the DNA sequences that it contains. In other words, it would imply that we knew all about embryogenesis and all about control mechanisms. But this is very far in the future. Nevertheless, one very important consequence of complete technical mastery is that we could design modified organisms or produce combinations of characteristics that would be quite impossible ever to have been produced by evolution. During the evolution of a highly specialized structure, each intermediate stage must, in its time, have had a selective advantage. This fact has limited the kinds of adaptations that can be made, since many highly adaptive end products could only be reached through deleterious intermediate stages. However, instead of this limited evolutionary process of stepwise mutation and selection, complete technical mastery would permit us to conceive a goal and achieve it directly without having to worry about whether the intermediate stages are disadvantageous. We could, for example, produce an organism that combines the happy qualities of animals and plants, such as one with a large brain so that it can indulge in philosophy and also a photosynthetic area on its back so that it would not have to eat. It is not inconceivable that there could be humanoids with chlorophyll under their skins so that they would look like the enormous green man on a can of peas.

Instead of a complex photosynthetic system, we might insert into the human genome a DNA sequence that will code for cellulase. In that case the individuals would be able to eat paper or sawdust because they would have cellulase to digest it, as cows and termites already can do with the help of microorganisms. Of course, at our present stage of knowledge, even if we could incorporate genes we would be unable to arrange for their expression in the right cells at the right time.

Another problem deserves comment. How can a layman judge the stage of technical feasibility if he does not follow the field very closely? For one thing, he can read the *Scientific American,* which is how I learn astronomy. And he can follow what is being done with domestic animals and plants. He will find that selective breeding is still the principal mode of operation.

Finally, I want to comment on the difference, if any, between the moral and ethical considerations pertaining to changing human heredity by direct intervention as opposed to changing it just by selection. I think that the restriction of individual freedom accompanying use of direct genome alteration is much less than it is by selective breeding methods. This may encourage us to try to overcome great technical difficulties. In the past selective breeding has been rejected (except by royalty, as Szybalski says) because of its potential limitation of personal freedom. So the question will arise: to what degree should individual freedom be restricted in order to make genetic improvements in the human species? I imagine Dr. Muller will have something to say about that in his chapter.

Dr. Rollin D. Hotchkiss

Dr. Sonneborn has asked us to consider whether man can and will change his own inheritance, to go beyond the limits suggested in the Bible and "by taking much thought unto himself add even so much as a cubit to his stature." Drs. Luria and Tatum have both indicated in how many ways man's thought has already led him to alter the heredity of microorganisms. Having participated in the modification of bacterial inheritance, I should like to give my present impressions of the prospects facing man.

Before discussing the methods and possibilities of genetic manipulation, let us consider first the broader question of whether, and why, man might indulge in it at all. Without doubt, many of us feel instinctive revulsion at the hazards of meddling with the finely balanced and far-reaching systems that make an individual what he is. Yet I believe it will surely be done, or attempted. The pathway will, like that leading to all of man's enterprise and mischief, be built from a combination of altruism, private profit, and ignorance.

It is not hard to point out worthwhile biological and medical ends: to repair nature's ravages or inequities, to restore what man has damaged or unbalanced (including perhaps through his self-imposed radiation), to build tissues more capable than those which existed before. The impetus, unlike that which developed atomic weapons, will not be political, but rather commercial. In a country where, during every waking moment, one is being told to acquire and enjoy the products of industrial ingenuity, we can well expect that one will be told he owes it to himself to improve his own genes, as well as his neighbor's! And governments will not want to stand in the way of such initiative—unless informed thinking on the part of the public is strongly unfavorable to it.

We have never hesitated to improve on nature for our shelter, clothing, and even food. We exercise our muscles to make them grow. We cannot resist interfering with the heritable traits of a phenylketonuric infant by feeding him tyrosine at the right time to form a normal nervous system, if we know that by not doing so we deprive him for life of this privilege. When we think that by interfering with the genetic substance, nucleic acids, we will principally affect the rapidly dividing cancer cells, we put hundreds of people to work making and testing suitable poisons.

So, we are going to yield when the opportunity presents itself. But genetic modifications might also come about accidentally through unanticipated effects of known agents. When in our laboratory we purposely destroyed with antibiotics certain sensitive bacteria in the presence of surviving resistant ones, we found that gene material from the former would enter and permanently change the latter cells. Others have found recently that three or four antibiotics that were being considered for their chemotherapeutic possibilities had pronounced effects on structure and integrity of DNA, the genic substance in the cells, and, therefore, interfered with its action. Such influences well might alter chromosome number or gene balance by rearranging genic substance in the differentiated tissues. If the causative agents were utilized for some accompanying beneficial effects, it would be true that the genetic manipulation, though unplanned, was willfully brought about.

How are we to caution an impatient altruism, curb an over-enthusiastic self-interest, or offset an uninformed interventionism? Obviously, by being, all of us, better informed. The scientists must think conscientiously about the far-reaching consequences and, I repeat, the economic, rather than political, forces that will be set in motion by any accomplishments in this direction. And having thought, scientists must speak (as they are doing here), not waiting as their discipline has tended to teach them to do, until they are absolutely sure before warning of a danger. It will be well if the public, besides striving to keep abreast of science, will seek to understand the scientist—to see him as the student he usually is, moving step by inevitable step toward what he feels must be understood if we are to advance. It is a disservice to society, the educational system, and communication if we see the scientist as the press often pictures him, a high priest moving in intuitive leaps about the dark recesses of unexplored knowledge, who from time to time opens a closet and there uncovers a brightly lighted, pre-existing arrangement of matter or principle, fully interpretable now that it has been "discovered."

As a student, then, and likely to both agree and disagree with the other scholars, we will leave the question of motivation and attempt to assess the possibilities that human inheritance can be manipulated constructively. So much of what Drs. Luria, Tatum, and Atwood have said seems accurate and incisive to me that I will mainly assume the same facts and offer my own independent evaluation.

First, let me present considerations that seem to argue that genetic engineering may be feasible. Emphatically, the principles found applicable to microorganisms will apply also to cells of man and the animals. Experiments and techniques are quickly tried out on the rapidly growing microorganisms, and, as other participants stated, cultures of human cell lines are available for ultimate testing. Dr. Tatum has offered very logical sequences in which such manipulations might move progressively toward control of germ lines and heredity. As both he and Dr. Luria have appropriately pointed out, the efficiency of gene transfer processes can probably be raised (by use of episomes, selective viruses, or imposed cell synchrony); also new types of carrier or mutator might be found (repressors, initiators, specific mutagens, antibiotics). Certainly, in principle, mutant viruses—or even mutant sperm—could be produced and should be relatively efficient. I should like to develop a related idea that new episomes or viruses might virtually be designed. Since such agents always have some homology with the host cell genome, it seems that they might be constructed by attaching to host DNA in vitro the chosen heterologous or modified genic material. Whether this were done by recombination in cells or by enzymes in test tubes, it could probably be done repetitively, and expanded fairly generally also to cover many traits. Control of the sex ratio, suggested by Dr. Atwood, would seem a fairly simple example for testing these approaches. It also brings up the further idea that, once we have specific reagents recognizing particular DNA sizes or arrangements, sperm might be "screened" for presence or absence of particular parental chromosomes, besides the sex chromosomes, thus guaranteeing which grandparent the offspring would follow in specific paternal traits.

As another source of specific substances that might modify genetic material, one might suggest the several enzymes that have specific affinities by which they recognize polynucleotides and react with them. These include the specific amino acid-activating enzymes and the DNA and RNA polymerases. Since the latter can modulate nucleotide structure in response to a nucleotide pattern or template, it is possible to conceive of polymerases that have a previously chosen template already attached to them and would go on to make a predesigned DNA or RNA within the cell.

Certainly, fractionation with replication of specific DNA molecules in vitro is even more likely within reach, as both Drs. Luria and Tatum have said. And it is possible that the molecular biologist might design a cofactor that could alter the shape or flow behavior of DNA molecules so that they could enter cells more effectively. We can already estimate quantitatively the efficiency of DNA transformations of bacteria in terms of physicochemical affinities of fixation, rates of penetration, rates and probabilities of recombination. This means that we can seek and select for higher efficiency in each of these three or four aspects of the process.

So, there are many suggestions as to how genetic engineering may be possible. Now, let us deal with some of the obstacles that lie in these paths.

While the principles of genetic functioning may be alike in all cells, the specific manifestations of these principles in microorganisms and human or other cells take special forms. (It is in fact the scientist's main problem to distinguish the fundamental principles from the elegant variations they take on in the concrete matter he studies.) Human cells have different cellular, and nuclear, membranes than bacteria, their chromosomes seem more complex, they are slower-growing and might break down added nucleic acid before it could affect them. They are diploid most of the time, so dominance and recessiveness may have to be dealt with. I cannot quite agree with Dr. Tatum that in diploids, our interest in recessives imposes a severe limitation, for double transformation, or diploidization, or segregation might also be inducible; but especially because it is often the double recessive that we would be most anxious to modify. And when we were setting out to modify an individual bearing both recessive and dominant genes, it would probably mean that we wanted to affect the progeny, which would certainly be possible. It should be mentioned that Dr. Ottolenghi and I tried for several months to use all our experience with bacteria to transform a dominant color trait into mouse embryonic cells, but could not demonstrate a single transformed cell among several thousand treated. Probably DNA uptake requires a kind of ingestion or pinocytosis; this may not be equally possible for different kinds of cells to carry out.

When one rightly says that the efficiency of transformation, and so forth, has been increased materially, one must bear in mind that this is mostly by providing specific influences for specific systems. We have increased the efficiency of transformation more than 100-fold over the years, but this is by adjusting the environment, timing, and selection to the strains at hand. Although these have helped with almost all markers, they have had much less effect on efficiency in other strains or species. Many factors at least will have to be worked out separately for each new application. This will probably be true for viruses, which are characteristically host-specific, and the highly efficient, but still not understood, transfer of episomes has also been evolved only within very small families in a very few host species; so again, we cannot speak of efficiency in a general sense as yet. To select for efficient target cell lines would defeat the purpose of learning to manipulate a given kind of cell. At present, the confused state of the chromosomes in most tissue cell cultures means too that these are not now ready as good test systems. We can also question how far a differentiated culture line of cells will serve adequately at all for pretesting the effect of genes to be introduced into an intact human body. One does not find this possible in general with drugs, and it could be very serious for genes which have the awesome property of amplifying their effect by getting themselves reproduced. Ominous things could happen in the first systems transferred from culture cells to the whole body, which would oblige us to devise much more cautious and laborious tests of safety.

We can expect things to move rather fast nowadays when followed continuously, but it may be worth mentioning that transformation, demonstrated in an animal experiment, was reduced to the test tube and recognized as attributable to DNA only by the sixteenth year, then in seven more years shown to apply to a variety of other traits, some of which could be quantitated. In the 12 years since, linkages and other parallels with classical genetics were shown and made the tools of what we have learned about mechanism.

For most of the viral, episomal, and chemical processes proposed for genetic engineering, there are three stages: interaction with the cell, penetration, reaction with the genome. For all of the polynucleotide-dependent processes, transformation work already mentioned suggests that the first two stages are uniquely governed by species- and cell-limited factors. The last "reaction," recombination for example, seems to require a large region of carrier polynucleotide for specific pairing, from which only a small and rather randomly chosen part is actually genetically effectively used. Choosing the right part from the right carrier will have to be quantitatively a far more selective event in the large amount of DNA present in human and animal cells.

One of my colleagues reveals to us that he does not know when biological engineering will be applied to man, but that he would not be surprised if it is sooner than he expects! I seem, in terms of techniques, to be saying that I know some working principles by which it could be done, but I do not see how it will be possible to do it!

In distributing accumulated experience and fruits of productivity to the untutored young, the undeveloped, and otherwise preoccupied persons, one of the great tasks of a civilized society is to engage in planning for future experience. One form of planning is scientific research. Another is to have the kind of responsible discussion we are recording here, and I am glad indeed that this one has been held. The dangers of genetic manipulation are great, and at present so are the difficulties that stand in its way. But I am sure time will steadily diminish the difficulties—and it is not a bit too soon to consider seriously and begin to diminish the dangers to which this course will expose us.

Dr. Klein

To discuss a subject that may not be as dangerous as some of the others, I shall start with euphenics which we will later avoid. There have been some very important successes in the transplantation field, but I would like to introduce a few words of caution in regard to the possibility of using transplantation in euphenic engineering.

Of course, there are two things one would like to do: (1) replace by transplantation something that is missing or defective, for instance a kidney or antibody-forming cells; and (2) eliminate something that is undesirable, such as a tumor that is antigenic, by adding cells that can form antibodies against those tumors and eliminate them.

What are the possibilities on the basis of what we now know about transplantation genetics in experimental animals? The genetically determined antigenic differences between different individuals of the same mammalian species are extremely numerous. There are not just a few. Some of the antigens are very strong, some of them weaker; but there are many. What then of the possibility, mentioned by Dr. Tatum, of obtaining a nonantigenic cell by recombination? I would like to suggest that this is impossible. The differences are so numerous that the probability of success would be like that for producing by mutation not a black mouse from a brown mouse but an elephant from a mouse. I do not think this is feasible.

A second possibility to be considered is to start with an antigenic cell and try to induce tolerance or paralysis against this cell type so that when used in transplantation it will be tolerated and accepted by the host. Now immunological tolerance and paralysis have been shown to occur even in adult animals in some very exceptional situations where you have very few, very weak antigenic differences between host and recipient. But, as soon as the differences are numerous and you are dealing with an adult (which will have to be dealt with in the human species), the difficulties are tremendous, and we have no clue at all that these are possible to solve.

Finally, we have the reaction, as far as antibody-forming cells are concerned, of the graft against the host. There is more hope that this difficulty can be overcome, for indications exist that some tolerance can be induced; but until this is fully achieved, transplantation of antibody-forming cells will make the recipients into immunological cripples. I should like to suggest, therefore, that major success with euphenic engineering by transplantation is improbable.

A much more reasonable probability would be to produce individuals by parthenogenesis, as Dr. Atwood has suggested, so that mothers would have parthenogenetic young. They would all be females of course. This would eliminate the males completely from the population. They would not be necessary after all. Then you could transplant anything you like from the parthenogenetic daughters back to the mother. This would keep the mother alive for a very long time. I suggest that this is a more realistic possibility than euphenic engineering by transplantation.

Dr. Atwood. I agree with you. It was in order to get around this problem completely that I suggested using the patient's own cells in my scheme for curing orotic aciduria. But as to having populations of females only, would it not be better just to have one parthogenetic daughter for each female, to supply her with transplants?

Dr. Klein: Who keeps the males alive?

Dr. Atwood: They would be as badly off as they are now.

Dr. DeMars: Dr. Atwood thought that use of the techniques of euphenic engineering might be less restrictive of the rights or privileges of the individual than use of techniques of eugenic breeding. To me it seems that the problems are exactly the same. Why do you make this distinction?

Dr. Atwood. If you want to change the human genome significantly by the process of selection, it takes quite a long time. You have to force people to breed in a directed manner. This has generally been repugnant to people and I suspect that many would object to this but would have no objection to equivalent alterations of their DNA accomplished through technical means.

Dr. Muller: I only want to register my disagreement with the stultifying assumption (made also in Medawar's *The Future of Man*) that people would have to be forced, rather than inspired, to engage in any effective kind of genetic betterment. I shall discuss this more fully later.

Question from the audience directed to Dr. Luria. How could coded or complex mutagens alter DNA in exactly the way desired?

Dr. Luria. I did not spell that out in full because it seemed to me that the most important thing to make clear was that for a molecule to distinguish one gene from another, it must be extremely complicated. Dr. Tatum has also commented on this. Two ideas are involved in the coded or complex mutagen. The first is that the total molecule would have to be so designed as to "recognize" one and only one gene among all those present in the cell. "Recognize" means in this case to be bonded together chemically after random collision, and in such a manner that each particular sequence of bases in the DNA of the gene is always bonded to a particular corresponding sequence of atomic groupings in the mutagen molecule. That is the sense in which the mutagen molecule is coded. There must be a close correspondence between the linear sequence of bases in the DNA of that gene and the linear sequence of atomic groupings in the mutagen molecule. Obviously, for the mutagen to be specific for one gene, it must match a sufficient length of the gene's DNA so that it would not be very similar to the sequence in an equal length of any other gene. Because there are only four principal bases in DNA, it might well require a long sequence of them to be sufficiently unique. That is the sense in which the mutagen must be complex.

The second idea is that the mutagenically active atomic grouping in the immense mutagen molecule must be inserted at exactly the right spot. Suppose, for example, one wished to mutate the base located as the one hundred fifty-first base from one end of the gene. Then one would have to put an active mutagenic grouping into the complex coded whole mutagenic molecule in exactly the position to bring it into contact with base number 151 when the long coded mutagen molecule pairs up point for point with the genic DNA. These are the main ideas, but of course they are only general ideas and many details important for their success remain to be worked out.

Question from audience. Would it not be better to use antigens rather than antibodies as selective mutagens?

Dr. Luria. This is a very interesting idea. It has not yet been determined whether an antigen itself persists when the antibody against it continues to be formed throughout the life of an organism. If antigens do persist and antibodies against some of them are mutagenic, it might be possible to introduce such antigens from outside and so obtain continuous production of mutagen. However, I do not know that one could expect such antibodies to have an affinity for one specific gene.

Question from audience. Do the things that are known for bacteria and viruses have application to mammalian cells? For example, has the mechanism of messenger production been validated for mammalian cells?

Dr. Luria. Evidence is accumulating very rapidly for the existence in mammalian cells of messenger RNA with the same kind of relationship to its DNA as the messenger RNA in bacteria has to its DNA. It is true (and I think Dr. Hotchkiss was one of the first to point this out at a meeting in 1962) that for quite a while many people used the term "messenger RNA" loosely, extrapolating from observations in which a certain fraction of RNA from mammalian cells resembles messenger RNA of bacterial cells. Now the evidence is becoming more abundant and more precise that these types of RNA are in fact the ones that control production of specific proteins once they become associated with the ribosomes.

Question from audience. How does carrier or transfer RNA differ from messenger RNA and why does it not make polypeptide also?

Dr. Luria. Carrier RNA, which according to the best evidence is produced under the control of specific genes, differs from messenger RNA by its internal structure. This structure is at least part of the reason that it fails to make protein. Along most of its length, carrier RNA appears to be bent back upon itself like a twisted hairpin. The two arms of the hairpin are double-bonded internally so that the bases in carrier RNA are not available for copying by the translation mechanism of a stretched-out RNA. Also, it is now widely held that in order to function as messenger, an RNA molecule must probably have some peculiar singularity at the beginning which in effect says: "Start here reading and translating into protein." But this is not yet known with certainty.

Question from audience. In their visions of the possibilities of "engineering" on man based on knowledge of viruses and bacteria, have not Drs. Tatum and Luria ducked the moral and ethical aspects?

Dr. Luria. Yes, I think that in the matter of responsibility and the kind of obligation that this places on biologists, many of the things that have been said may sound a little callous. However, our task was to discuss only the technicalities of work that could conceivably be done. Actually, we have already overstepped our assignment quite a bit by all of our warnings. I expect that the ethical and moral issues will be the topics of much discussion later.

PART II

Human Cell Cultures

CHAPTER 3

Investigations in Human Genetics with Cultivated Human Cells: A Summary of Present Knowledge

Robert DeMars, Department of Medical Genetics
University of Wisconsin

The breath-taking advance of molecular genetics has depended on especially favorable manipulative properties of microorganisms. Its influence on the study and possible management of human heredity, for good or ill, will be limited by the ability to perform experiments with man much like those that have been performed with microbes. Information about heredity is usually obtained by performing breeding experiments in which the inheritance of traits is studied with intact individuals. Controlled breeding experiments are not feasible with man, and much of the desired information is gained by observation, catch-as-catch-can, of the outcomes of his rather haphazardly pursued breeding activities. This is an exceedingly cumbersome and time-consuming procedure and pretty much excludes the large variety of experiments that have been performed with microbes. There would be a real premium on circumventing ordinary breeding in the study of human heredity, regardless of special applications of such studies.

A partial solution to this problem lies in regarding the human body as a population of cells, rather than as a unit. In partly divorcing hereditary analysis from work with individuals one could add to the variety of genetic experiments that can be performed and to the types of information obtained. The isolation of cells from the body and their propagation in the laboratory permits one to study certain aspects of human heredity in much the same way that one would study bacteria. The results of such studies would be expressed in terms of the transfer of hereditary determinants from a cell to its progeny cells instead of from human beings to their offspring. One could obtain information as valid and more varied than that gained from breeding experiments. The analogies between cultures of human cells and cultures of microbes are so important that they merit review here, for they mean that we may witness another surge in the advance of genetic knowledge, this time in the area of human genetics.

The cultures are commonly started from a small bit of skin the size of a match head. Occasionally a tumor or some other tissue is used as starting material. The bits of tissue are introduced into culture vessels containing a complex nutrient solution, the composition of which is based on that of blood serum. They attach to the glass or plastic surface of the vessel, and within a few days cells begin to migrate out of the tissue and proliferate while attached to the surface (Plate 1*A*). In a few weeks the original bit of tissue is surrounded by a dense halo of growth that may contain hundreds of thousands of cells (Plate 1*B*). In order to maintain further rapid growth the cells must be removed from the surface, dispersed as a suspension, and used as inocula for new cultures. In this way the population density can be reduced, and a repeating cycle of proliferation, dispersal, and subculture is initiated. Generally, it is convenient to handle the populations of cells so that they increase 10- to 20-fold in a one-week interval separating successive subcultures (Plate 2*A, B*), although this does not represent the maximum rate at which the cells can multiply.

Focus now on a single cell in such a population. Within a few hours after its removal from the glass and separation from its neighbors it can be observed, reattached, and isolated (Plate 3*A, B*). Human cells, being much larger than bacteria, can easily be observed with less than one tenth as much magnification, i.e., with a magnification of about 75-fold. The cell divides for the first time in about a day (Plate 3*C*), the two daughter cells divide a day later (Plate 3*D*), and the population thus initiated doubles again and again about once a day (Plates 3*E, F, G*), although all the cells do not divide synchronously. All the cells remain in the same vicinity because of their attachment to the surface of the culture vessel and their limited ability to move about. The result of this, in two weeks, is a colony about one-eighth to one-quarter inch in diameter that contains several thousand cells. The cells in the colony can then be

[*Text continued on p. 55.*]

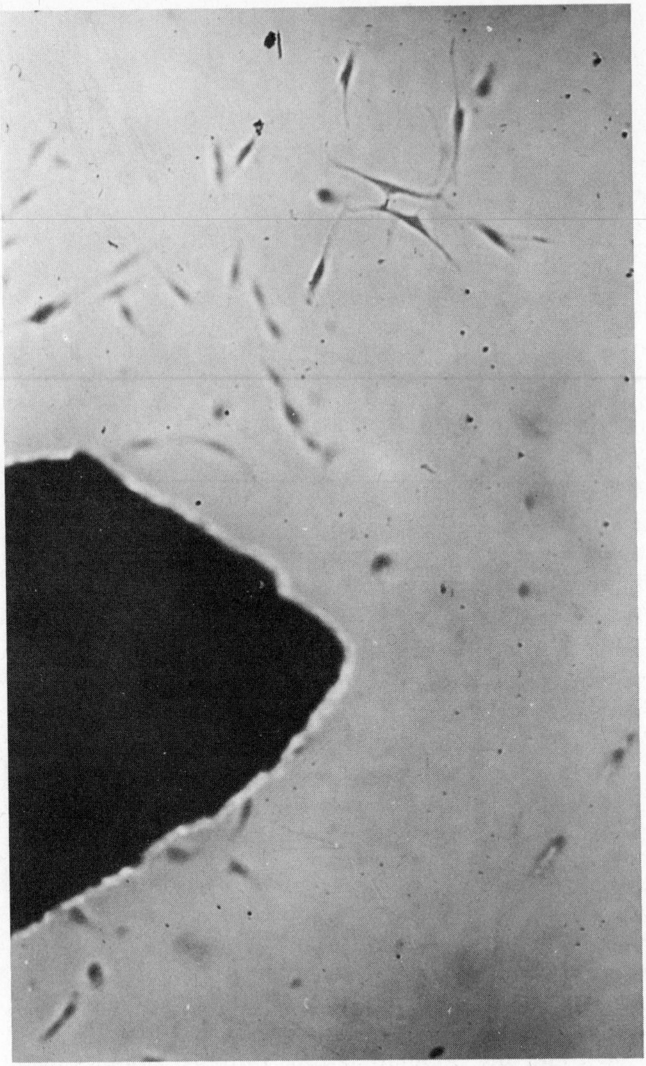

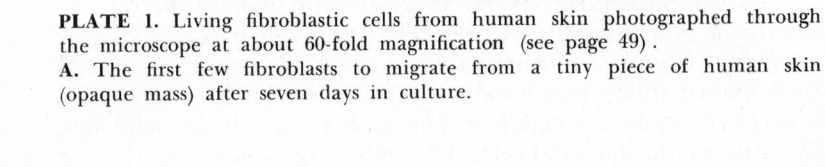

PLATE 1. Living fibroblastic cells from human skin photographed through the microscope at about 60-fold magnification (see page 49).
A. The first few fibroblasts to migrate from a tiny piece of human skin (opaque mass) after seven days in culture.

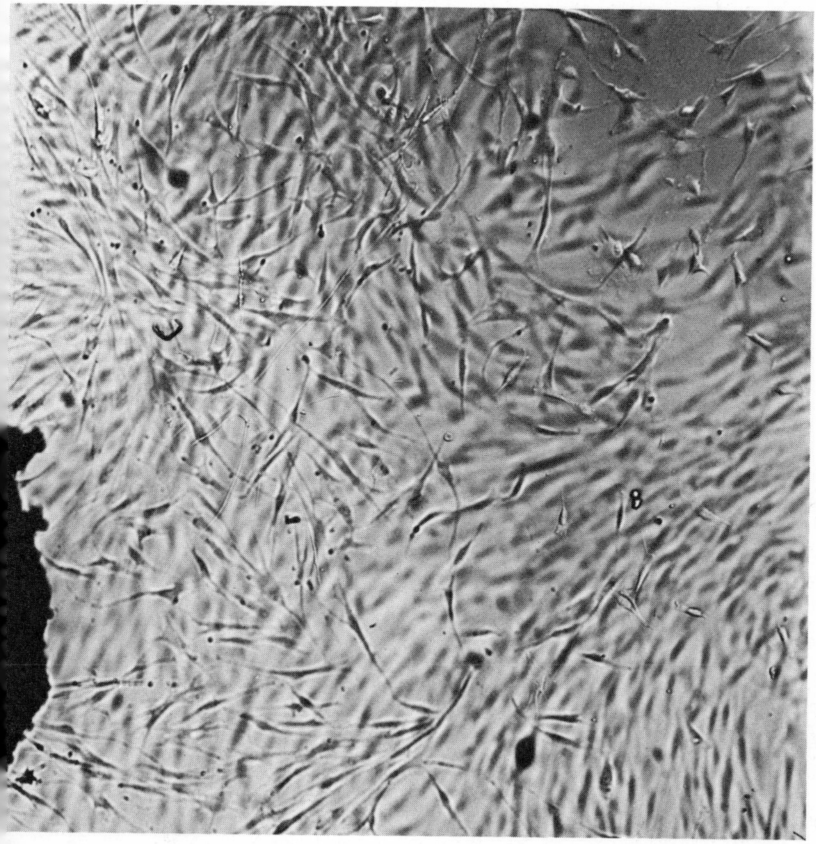

B. A similar piece of skin after 21 days in culture. The skin was surrounded by a halo of thousands of fibroblastic cells. At this stage the cells are removed from the glass bottom of the culture vessel, dispersed, and inoculated into a new culture vessel containing fresh culture medium.

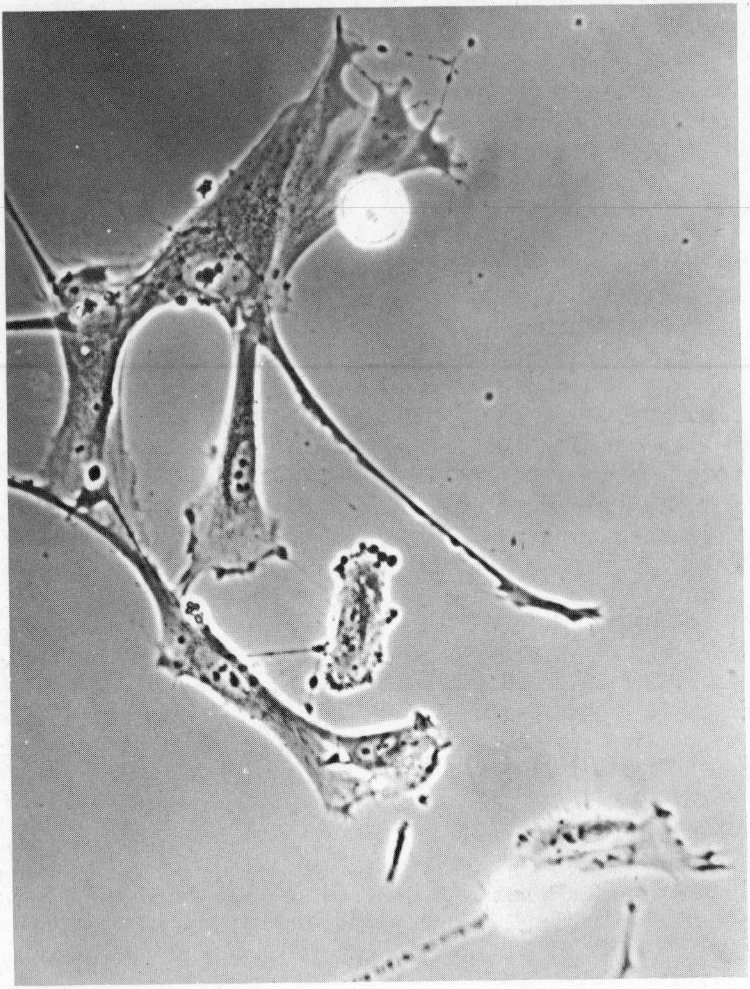

PLATE 2. Living fibroblastic cells from human skin, magnified about 200-fold, one- and seven-day-old subcultures (see page 49).

A. One day after dispersal, dilution, and transfer from an old to a new growth flask. The cells were flat with the exception of the spherical cell showing a bright halo, which was dividing. Much of the glass surface available for growth was unoccupied.

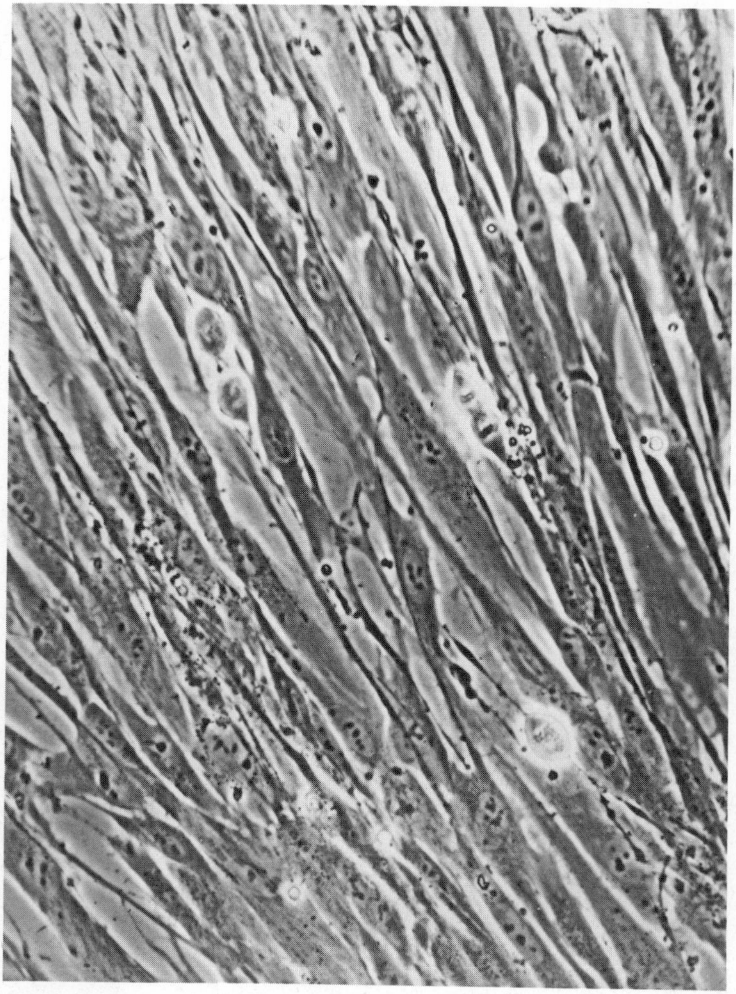

B. The same portion of the culture flask photographed seven days later, after several renewals of the culture medium. The fibroblasts had proliferated and formed dense, parallel arrays covering all the available surface. Several dividing cells were visible.

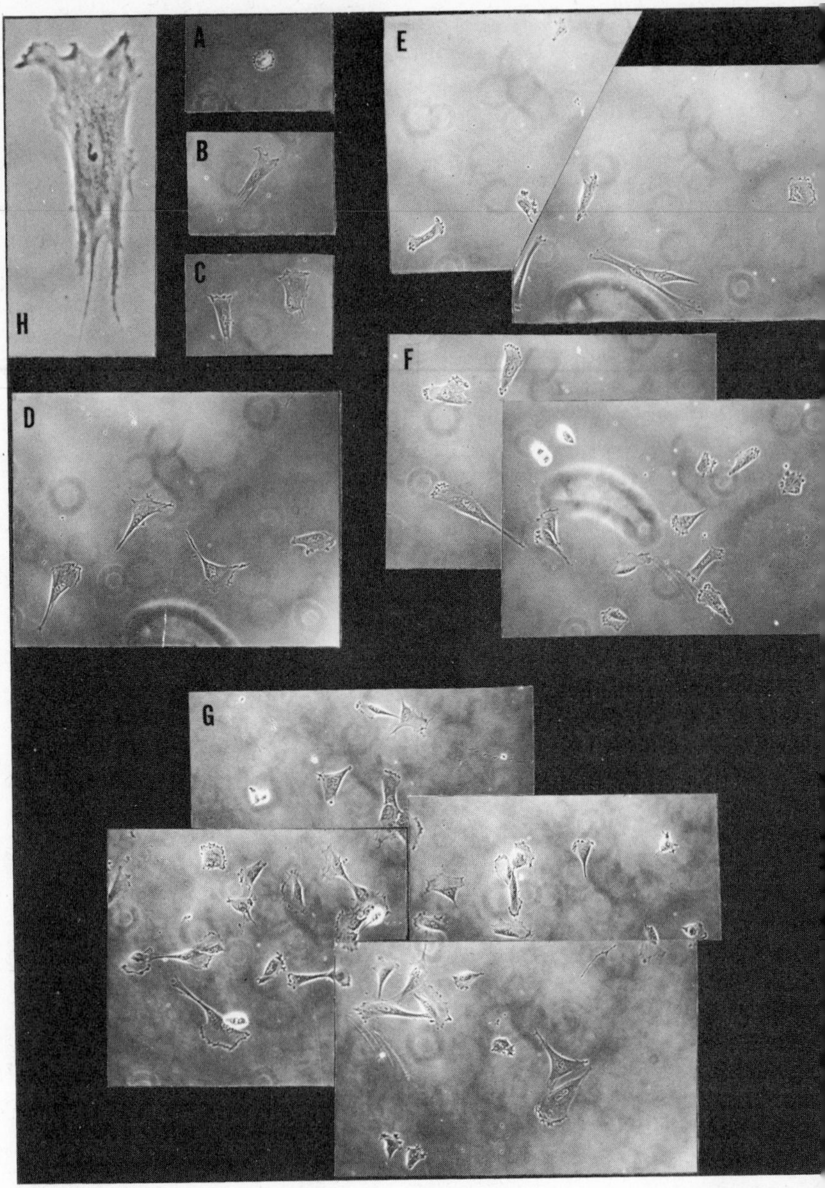
A
B
C
D
E
F
G
H

dispersed and their propagation resumed. If all goes well, a single cell can produce a progeny of about a million cells in four weeks, and the cycle of subculture previously described can be started.

This brief history contains several points of great importance. The populations of cells derived from a single cell are called clones and are a necessary tool for much genetic work. Because chromosomes generally produce replicas just like themselves which are then, as a rule, equally distributed to the two daughter cells at each cell division, the cells of a clone are genically identical except for rare cases of mutation. The rapidity with which the cells proliferate minimizes the interval between the initiation of an experiment and the acquisition of the results. The minimum pertinent interval here is the time necessary to produce enough progeny cells to display the heritable characteristics under study. In some special cases, the characteristics of a single progeny cell can be observed, and the results are therefore obtained in a day or two. Usually, this cannot be done and inferences are made about the properties of the individual cells under study by examining the properties of the progeny population in a visible colony, as a whole. This procedure

PLATE 3. The beginning of a clone of diploid human cells. The time intervals given below are the numbers of hours that elapsed between the isolation of the original single cell and the time the photographs were taken.
(Photographs made with a phase contrast microscope in a Sykes-Moore perfusion chamber. The images of **A** through **G** are about 100 times life size, while the image of **H** is about 400 times life size.)
A. The cell was isolated by dispersing a population of cells and diluting the resulting suspension so that only one cell was placed in a chamber suitable for microscopic observation of living cells. After five hours the cell had reattached to the thin glass wall of the observation chamber but had not yet become flat.
B. The same cell flattened, 11 hours after isolation.
C. By 29 hours the cell had divided, forming two daughter cells.
D. Each daughter cell had divided again by 49 hours, producing four cells altogether.
E. After 73 hours the four cells had become eight. Note that the fibroblasts can move about slightly on glass surfaces so that clones are usually rather diffuse in their initial stages of development. This necessitated the use of photographs of two or more overlapping microscopic fields of view in order to record all the cells.
F. Sixteen cells at 97 hours.
G. The 44 progeny cells derived from the original cell 135 hours after its isolation. Rounded cells with bright halos in **F** and **G** were dividing. The cells become more densely packed as the clonal population grows. Finally, the cells appear as they do in Plate 2**B** and comprise a discrete colony that is ready for subculture.
H. An enlarged view of the single cell of **B.**

is, in effect, one of magnification; the traits of a single cell are, as it were, enlarged into the same traits of its numerous progeny. For some practical purposes, then, such a colony is treated as an individual, and one might compare the two-week interval necessary for the production of a visible colony of human cells with the nine-month interval necessary for the production of a child, and the advantage of the cultured cells in this respect becomes obvious.

Large populations of cells can be conveniently manipulated in culture. A single culture dish, 1 in. in diameter, may contain almost 1 million human cells growing as a thin film one cell deep on the glass. Each cell is the equivalent of an intact human for the purposes of certain genetic experiments. This is important because many of the genetic changes that are of interest occur with such low frequency that their detection depends on the examination of large populations.

The cells can be propagated in well-defined environments, permitting controlled variation of conditions to suit the purposes of the experimenter. This makes it possible to assess the validity of observations by determining if repetitions of the same experiment yield similar results. It also facilitates reliable comparisons between different strains of cells or between the effects of different treatments on the cells.

Another important aspect of the ability to vary the culture environment can best be made clear by referring again to the necessity of working with large populations of cells, numbering in the millions, in order to detect and study rare genetic variants. How are the rare cells detected? Clearly, it is practically impossible to examine each cell individually until the cells of interest are found. This procedure could be compared to trying to call a friend in New York City, not knowing his telephone number, when the only directory available had all the numbers listed but none of the corresponding names. Much genetic variation in man is detected because it leads to illness or abnormality and the affected individuals come to the attention of a physician. In a sense, such genetic variants select themselves out of the population at large. The cultured cells cannot do this, and the experimenter must impose selective conditions that permit the rare genetic variants to stand out against the background of normal cells. The use of selection in studying genetic variation has been so fundamental in work with microbes and will play so important a role in work with cultured cells that it warrants a brief illustration here.

Amethopterin is a chemical agent often used in the treatment of leukemia. It interferes with an important step in the metabolic activities of human cells and prevents their proliferation. The lethal effects are most pronounced in cells that are reproducing rapidly, such as those in culture. Consider a population of 1 million cells growing attached to the inner glass surface of a culture vessel. The addition of amethopterin to the culture medium very quickly stops

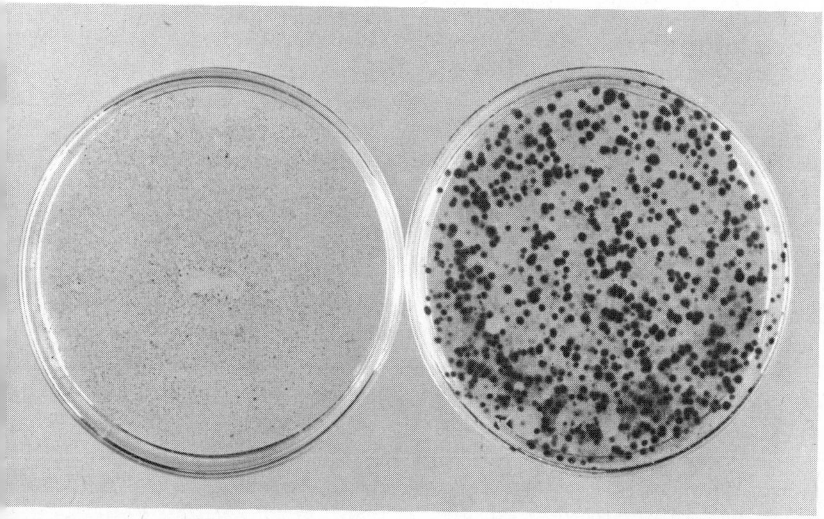

A B

PLATE 4. Cultures of HeLa (human cervical carcinoma) cells in Petri dishes. (About life size.) The populations of cells in both dishes were subjected to selection with amethopterin (see page 57). **A** did not contain mutants that could survive the treatment, and all that remained in the dish were some of the cells that had been killed. Population **B** contained many mutants resistant to the selective treatment, and these formed colonies visible to the naked eye. Both populations of cells were stained to make the cells more easily visible. (Reprinted by permission of The Rockefeller Institute Press, from R. DeMars and J. L. Hooper, A method of selecting for auxotrophic mutants of HeLa cells. *J. Exp. Med.*, 3:559, 1960. The photographs here reproduced from printed copy inevitably show a loss of detail, and quality of the result is not representative of the originals.)

their proliferation and, within a few days, causes them to become distorted. They permanently lose their capacity to reproduce, and within a week the majority actually become detached from the glass surface and are removed when the culture medium is renewed. If the treatment with amethopterin is continued, one may observe

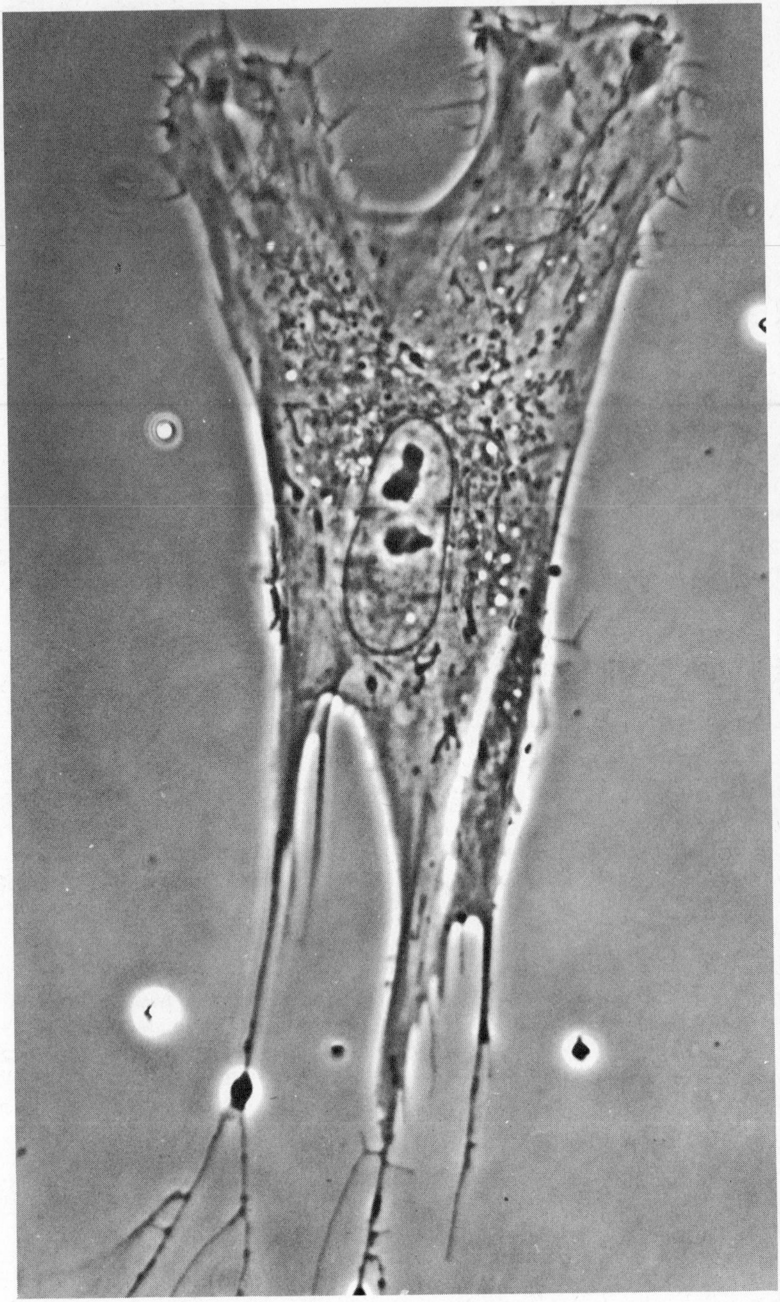

within about ten days perhaps ten patches of cells that are proliferating and that have formed colonies visible to the naked eye (Plate 4). The cells in these colonies can be isolated and, after further propagation in the absence of amethopterin, be shown to have acquired permanent resistance to the growth-inhibitory effects of the drug. All the evidence indicates that the resistant cells initiating formation of the colonies already existed in the population before treatment with amethopterin was begun.

This outline gives some idea of the infrequent occurrence of certain hereditary variants, about one per hundred thousand in this case. It also indicates how the geneticist can directly and, at the same time, blindly select for the rare, genetically altered cell he is interested in by inhibiting or killing all other cells with the appropriate selective condition. It was the application of exactly such selective procedures that permitted the isolation of many bacterial mutants, and that led to the initial detection of genetic recombination when the mutants were allowed to conjugate. Even earlier, selective methods helped in making the discovery that DNA was the genetic material of bacteria.

The specific example of selection with amethopterin has additional meaning. In practice, populations of leukemic blood cells treated in the body with the drug for the first time are sensitive to its inhibitory action and the leukemia is arrested. This remission is temporary, however, and, in time, the original population is replaced by one consisting of cells that can multiply in the presence of amethopterin. The nature of the change that occurs in the leukemic cells is not yet known in man, but selection experiments with cell cultures point to the obvious possibility that resistant mutants occur among leukemic cells and that they are selected out by amethopterin treatment. This is one instance where attempts

PLATE 5. One living cell cultivated from human skin and of a sort used for in vitro genetic studies. This diploid fibroblast is in the interphase stage of the cell life cycle. It is attached to the thin glass wall of an observation chamber filled with nutrient fluid. The sharply outlined oval within the cell is the nucleus, which contains the chromosomes. (Photographed with a phase-contrast microscope at 640 magnification; photograph enlarged to final magnification of about 1600-fold.)

The chromosomes exist as extended fibers that are so thin as to be invisible to the ordinary microscope. It is during interphase that the genes produce their products and the chromosomes are replicated. In preparation for mitosis the nuclear membrane disappears, the cell becomes rounded, and the chromosome fibers condense, becoming thicker and readily visible in the light microscope (see Plate **6**).

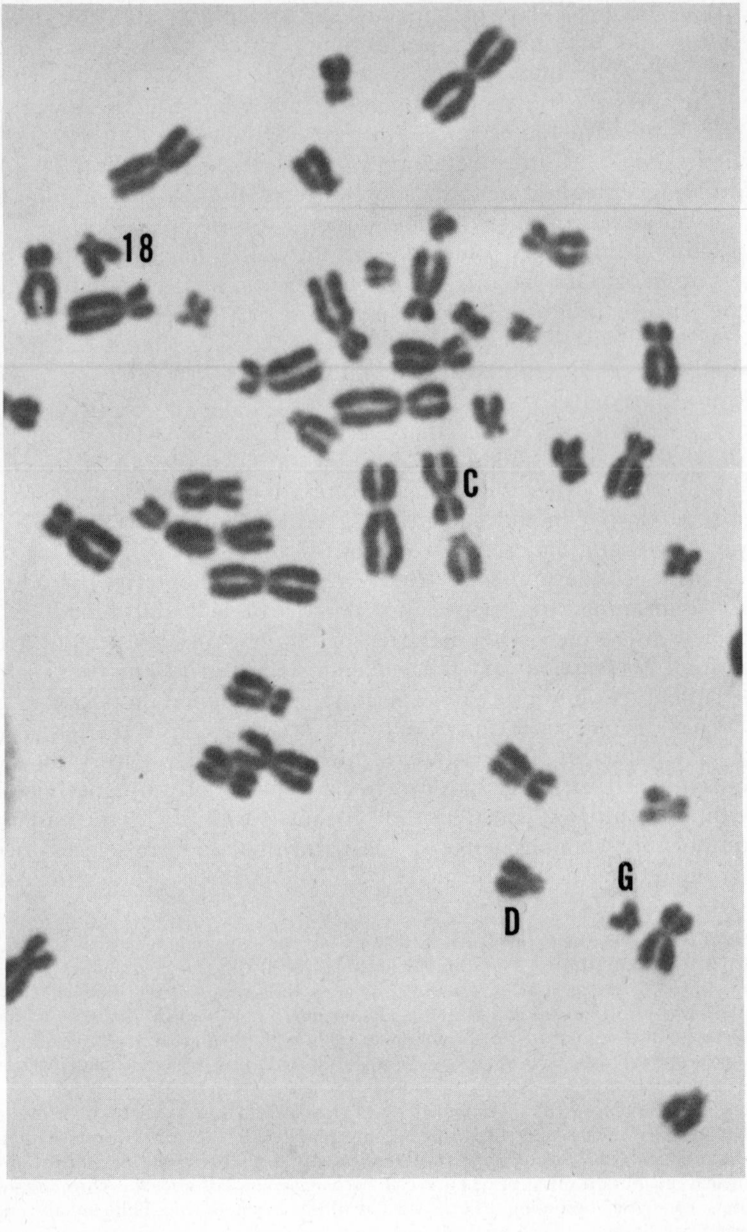
18
C
D
G

to understand our failures in treating leukemia may profit from regarding the human body as a population of cells that may contain a small proportion of hereditary variants of one sort or another. When selective conditions, such as drug treatments, are applied, these minority components of the cell population may be selected out and become the dominant type of cell. Such considerations emphasize the relation between the study of individuals and the study of populations of cells in culture. They indicate as well that selection is a process that may occur in the body as well as in a laboratory culture vessel.

Some attention should now be given to two manipulative aspects of cultured human cells that do not apply to microbes in as practical a manner. First, because the cells are larger than microbes, they can easily be observed and manipulated under the microscope (Plate 5). This permits the visual detection and recovery of certain genetically altered cells in the living state and satisfies a need that sometimes cannot be satisfied with the blind selective methods previously described. Second, it is not difficult to study the chromosomes of human cells. One can thus observe the physical basis of certain types of results of genetic experiments that involve changes in chromosome number or microscopically visible changes in chromosome morphology (Plate 6).

It has not been my aim to present a technical manual. Rather, I have attempted to create an impression of a new laboratory tool, the cultured human cell, and of the similarities between such cells and microbes as especially advantageous objects of genetic research. One can add that the study of heredity with intact human beings has dealt mainly with characteristics that are the end points of the differentiative changes occurring during development. The relation

PLATE 6. The normal chromosomes of man, as found in a diploid cell dividing in culture. (Photograph by courtesy of Dr. Klaus Patau.) The chromosome complement of man consists of one pair of sex-determining chromosomes and 22 pairs of other chromosomes, called autosomes. One member of each pair is derived from each parent of an individual. Females derive an X chromosome from both parents and are XX, whereas males derive a Y instead of an X from their fathers and are, therefore, XY. These chromosomes illustrate the difficulty in reliably identifying every chromosome of any individual human cell. The X is a "C"-like chromosome and, ordinarily, cannot be unambiguously identified in every cell. The Y is a "G"-like chromosome but is usually distinctive enough to be reliably identified. Another "G"-like chromosome causes Down's syndrome when present in triplicate instead of duplicate. Other syndromes of congenital abnormalities are caused by the presence, in triplicate, of a "D"-like chromosome or of chromosome number 18.

between such characteristics and the immediate expression of gene action, the production of specific proteins, is almost completely unknown at present. In contrast, the relative simplicity of the cultured cell forces the geneticist to concentrate on many cellular characteristics that more immediately reflect the activities of the genes. This sets the stage for the cooperative biological and chemical analysis that forged the framework of modern molecular genetics.

A final point: The similarities in the methods of handling human cells and of handling microbes lead one to expect similarities in the kinds of experiments that have been performed and in the kinds of information obtained with the two types of organisms. These same similarities in methodology have also imposed shared limitations on what can and cannot be done. However, the organisms are very different, and investigators would be remiss in not anticipating and, even, seeking differences, as well as similarities, in their genetic behavior.

Consider now whether the anticipated harvest of new genetic knowledge is being reaped by those working with cultured cells. A brief examination of the results so far suggests that this is so. Experiments with selection have resulted in the isolation of several different kinds of variants that are resistant to growth-inhibitory agents. One of the agents used is puromycin (1), an antibiotic that blocks protein synthesis. Others, such as 8-azaguanine (2) and 6-mercaptopurine, interfere with the normal synthesis of nucleic acids. Variants differing in nutritional requirements are known, as are strains differing in susceptibility to infection by certain viruses. Furthermore, controlled variation of the culture medium has already led to the discovery of several phenomena resembling the induction and repression of enzyme formation in bacteria.

The ability to assess the viability of individual cells by observing whether they can produce enough descendants to form a colony visible to the naked eye has been used to make detailed studies of the effects of radiations on human cells (3). The evidence indicates that much of the damage caused by X-rays occurs in the genetic material and that at least some of this is due to chromosome breakage. Evidence has even been obtained for cellular processes that repair radiation-induced damage (4).

Results resembling DNA-mediated transformations in bacteria have recently been reported (5) but have not yet been shown to be exactly the same kind of phenomenon. In these experiments, genetic material (DNA) was extracted from a strain of human cells having a characteristic hereditary trait that permitted it to grow in the presence of amethopterin. The DNA was made available to another strain of human cells that could not grow in the presence of the drug. By using selective techniques it was shown that some of the cells (about 1 in 10,000) exposed to the DNA, and the descendants of these cells, subsequently exhibited the trait that characterized the cell strain from which the DNA had been extracted.

Now if we agree that the advantages of working with cultured cells redound to work with cells from other organisms, as well as those from human beings, this catalogue of interesting genetic results can be lengthened. The infection of cells derived from chickens, hamsters, or mice with certain viruses results in their conversion to cancer cells (6). Lately, results that are similar in some ways have been obtained with virus infections of human cells (7). It has also just been discovered that the blood streams of children with typical measles virus infections have transiently high frequencies of blood cells with broken chromosomes (8). These different manifestations of virus infections in human cells may not be unrelated.

Finally, it is now known that cells of certain strains, derived from mice, can fuse, producing hybrid cells that combine the chromosome sets of the two parent cells (9, 10). Chromosomes are lost during the subsequent proliferation of these hybrids, so that the final result is cells having chromosome numbers roughly similar to those of the parent strains. These cells with reduced chromosome number may, nevertheless, still be hybrid, having some chromosomes characteristic of one parent strain and others characteristic of the second parent strain. Future work along these lines will involve the use of strains that differ with respect to known heritable traits as well as in the possession of morphologically distinctive chromosomes. Determination of the presence of particular traits and of particular chromosomes in the hybrid cells may then permit the assignment of the genetic determinants for the traits to distinctive chromosomes.

It is our task to try to anticipate the extent to which such studies will contribute to our knowledge of human heredity. It might be wise to examine some of the results described above in greater detail. This will grant us a realistic idea of what has happened and, perhaps, of what we may look forward to. The subject of the mutants found in cultures of human cells will be discussed first because the use of mutants is basic to all genetic work. The second concerns the DNA-mediated hereditary changes. They have great potential importance and their spectacular nature creates wide appeal for people who are spectators of, as well as for those active in, genetic work.

All the mutants of human cells that have been isolated by selection in the laboratory have been derived from cells that had abnormal sets of chromosomes. The numbers ranged between about 55 and over 80 per cell from strain to strain, although each strain had a characteristic number. The normal number is 46 (Plate 6). There are 23 pairs of chromosomes in the cells of females, including a pair of X chromosomes that determine femaleness. The cells of males have only one X, the second one being replaced by a chromosome called "Y", which is morphologically and functionally distinct. It determines maleness. The morphology of some human chromosomes is quite characteristic, but others of the set are so similar as to make them virtually indistinguishable from one another. This leads to a special difficulty in doing genetic experiments with the abnormal strains. It cannot be determined very well how many chromosomes of each kind are present, and, therefore, the number of copies of each gene is unknown. This uncertainty is aggravated by the possibility that segments of genetic substance have been transferred from one chromosome to another and that such translocated segments may go undetected. The properties of cells vary according to the dosage of genes, and the same gene may function differently in different chromosomal locations.

It is proper to ask if the altered properties of the mutants that have been selected might not be due to changes in the number of chromosomes or to rearrangements of the genetic material. There are at least three reasons for taking the first possibility seriously. First, the number of chromosomes per cell in the abnormal strains is not the same for all cells of a given strain, but varies by plus or minus several chromosomes from the average for the population (11). Therefore, there is no doubt that the numbers of certain chromosomes vary in these strains. Second, aminopterin-resistant mutants of human origin have been shown (12) to have characteristic chromosome makeups different from those of the sensitive, parent strains in which they originated. Third, one abnormal strain of human cells, having an average chromosome number in the 70's, yielded a mutant with average chromosome number 55 and at least three altered heritable traits: increased resistance to infection with polio virus, increased requirement of a nutrient called glutamine, and altered colony morphology. Simultaneous, multiple, and, apparently, unrelated changes of this sort are not expected to result from a single localized event called a mutation. They are just what is expected when large segments of genetic material or entire chromosomes are added to or subtracted from the cell, since this alters the dosage of many genes at once. It is also exactly what is found when human beings possess an extra chromosome, a third copy of one of the chromosomes that is normally present only in duplicate. Such triplication of one particular chromosome in man leads to the constellation of abnormalities called Down's syndrome or "mongolism" (13). For two other chromosomes, triplication results in multiple deviations from normal development, the assortment of abnormalities being characteristic for each of the chromosomes (14).

The variations in chromosome number that have been considered here result from accidents in the distribution of chromosomes during cell division. This type of accident, called "mitotic nondisjunction," alters the *amount* of genetic material, and must be distinguished from the localized changes in the *kind* of genetic material, which result in genic mutations. Each type of change results in cells with altered heritable characteristics. At this time we cannot define which type of change has led to the appearance of hereditary variants in cultured human cells. Evidently, some of them do arise through nondisjunction. It is also worth mentioning that attempts to isolate mutants from human cells having normal sets of chromosomes have failed so far, even though the types of mutants sought were exactly the same as those readily obtained from cultures of abnormal cells.

The experiments with DNA-mediated hereditary changes have relevance here. In bacteria, the genetic alterations effected by DNA are executed locally, changing the kind of genetic information residing in only a small region of the chromosome. This kind of knowledge is lacking in the analogous experiments performed with human cells. One might surmise that those mutant properties that are alterable by DNA are determined by localized mutations. This circular type of reasoning would not advance our understanding very far, especially since it is not even certain that the DNA actually causing the hereditary transformation has interacted with the chromosomes of the transformed cells. All that one can say now is that DNA effective in causing the appearance of certain specific traits in appropriate receptor cells (i.e., transformation) can be isolated only from donor cells that have those specific traits to begin with. Furthermore, cells that are transformed by DNA produce progeny that also have the new trait and that can serve as donors of DNA with transforming activity. This indicates that the transformation is propagated as genetic material of the cells. It remains to be seen if the DNA effects transformation by changing the kind of genetic information residing in a local region of a chromosome or whether some other kind of hereditary change is involved. Another consideration should be added here. Local changes in the kind of genetic information of bacteria can be effected either by DNA or by certain chemical agents effective in producing mutations. Attempts to produce mutations in human cells with some of the same chemical mutagenic agents have failed, even in the case of the only hereditary change that has so far proved to be alterable by DNA. Several explanations for this difference in behavior could be adduced. Perhaps it resides in the differences in chemical and physical organization that distinguish the chromosomes of human beings and bacteria, or that distinguish the cells, themselves. Clearly, our understandings of mutation and of DNA-induced hereditary changes are interdependent, and our uncertainties about them are likely to be resolved together.

Some other aspects of the experiments with DNA deserve mention, especially if comparisons are made with the experiments performed with microbes. The basic experiment with DNA-mediated genetic changes in bacteria involves the use of two strains distinguished by one or a few genetic differences, the remainders of their genetic materials being identical. DNA, representative of all the genetic material, is extracted from the donor strain and made available to intact cells of the receptor strain. The uptake of DNA by the receptor cells can be remarkably efficient, but the probability of occurrence of any particular genetic transformation is low so that the transformants are usually detected by selective methods. If the donor and receptor strains differ in several respects, then transformations for each of the differences can be detected in the receptor population, although, with certain special exceptions, it is very unusual for more than one to occur in the same cell. Therefore, the DNA extracted from donor cells is potentially capable of effecting many genetic changes, perhaps at any part of the genetic material, but the probability of occurrence of any particular change in a given cell is low. It is very likely that a significant fraction of a population of receptor cells incorporates genetic information from the donor cells. Almost all of these incorporations ordinarily go undetected in experiments with microbes because the DNA's of the donor and receptor cells contain identical genetic information except at the locus or loci being studied. Essentially the same description applies to the experiments with DNA and cultured human cells. In one important respect it does not apply to the transfer of DNA from cells of one human being to those of another. For, in general, each human being differs genetically from another in many respects, and the differences at present are defined to only a limited extent. In this case, for every receptor cell transformed at a particular locus there are probably many others transformed at other, generally undefined loci. For the time being, then, we have little or no control over the specificity of DNA-mediated genetic changes, and the numerical efficiency of the process is still very low.

My own summary of the work in the areas of mutation and DNA-mediated transformations in cultured human cells is that much has been achieved and little is really understood. These comments deal with the past and the present and may seem hypercritical. I would like to temper them with consideration of some aspects of the future. It should be clear that some of the dissatisfaction with the work that has been done arises in uncertainty about the nature of the "mutants" that have been isolated in cultures of human cells. In the history of other organisms, whose genetics is better understood, such uncertainties were at least partly resolved by breeding experiments, permitting the classification of hereditary changes in one category or another, such as genic mutation or nondisjunction. A thoroughgoing method of performing experiments that yield the same kind of information for cultured cells does not now exist. However, the study of mutation need not be stymied by the present lack of means for breeding analysis or effective substitutes for it. Man constantly provides breeding information about himself concerning differences that are genetically determined. These differences and the information about their hereditary transmission can be turned to account for the purpose of genetic studies with human cells provided (1) the differences have well-defined patterns of inheritance, and (2) the genetic differences are expressed as differing properties of the cells in culture.

Only a few heritable differences in man are now known to meet these requirements but the number may be expected to increase. It is already large enough for making progress. Congenital galactosemia (15) is one example. In this case mutations lead to loss of the capacity to produce a protein catalyst (enzyme) that is involved in the body's utilization of the sugar galactose. Milk is a rich source of galactose, and the inability of galactosemic children to use the sugar derived from this and other sources has a number of dire consequences. Unless galactose is removed from their diet, the children usually fail to thrive, and they develop cataracts and enlarged livers and may have subnormal mental development.

Obviously, none of these defects of the intact individual is manifested by cultured cells, but the absence of the enzyme called "transferase" is manifested in the cells in at least two ways. First, little or no enzyme activity can be detected in the cells. Second, the cells fail to grow if galactose is the only sugar provided in the nutrient medium, while cells with nonmutant genes have the enzyme, utilize the galactose, and grow (16). This situation is made to order for the study of mutation by applying selective methods. A population of cells derived from a galactosemic individual will fail to grow in a culture medium containing galactose as the sole sugar. If mutations that restore the capacity to produce the needed enzyme occur, the affected cells will grow and be selected for. The ability to select for mutations affecting this enzyme and our knowledge about the specific product (the enzyme) of the gene involved are two factors that make these mutations especially suitable for genetic analysis in cultured cells. Another such property is the fact that breeding analysis indicates that these are the kinds of mutations of greatest interest: local changes in the kind of genetic information.

Finally, these properties might permit pursuit of the work with DNA-induced changes in a way that would lead to less equivocal interpretation of the results. Galactosemia mutations are not the only ones that will be studied in this way but I believe they provide us with a model program for putting the study of mutation and DNA-induced changes in cultured cells on a surer footing. Exactly the same approach is being used by the students of mouse heredity when they study cells cultured from mice that vary in the genetic determinants of certain antigenic components of the cells (17).

The available evidence concerning the galactosemia mutations indicates that the product of the genes in which they occur is the "transferase" enzyme itself. Such genes, in general, are called "structural" genes because they determine the specific molecular structures of the proteins we study, such as enzymes. Work with microbes has made it abundantly clear that there is another general category of genes that may be called "regulators." Regulators control the degree of activity of structural genes and might be compared to on-off switches or rheostats that respond to specific stimuli from the environment. Genetic material determines not only what kinds of substances are produced but also the time, place, and quantity of their production. We do not know if regulators of the sort found in microbes occur in human genetic material but the necessity for schemes controlling gene action should be clear. How else could one understand the origin and function of the diverse, specialized cell types that arise during the development of the individual from a single cell, the fertilized ovum? The only general statement I wish to make on the subject of control is that we might expect to find several different expressions, if not types, of control schemes in human cells. I think many embryologists would consider the specific control over production of a single enzyme to be a type rather different from that determining the origin of white blood cells, for instance. Other examples of controls would be those regulating the timing for the production of gene products and for gene replication during the intervals between cell divisions.

We can ask about the kinds of control schemes that might be amenable to analysis with cells in culture. I think one of these will be that concerned with regulation of the production of enzymes. These schemes are of interest because different cells of the body are distinguished, not only by form, but also by specific patterns of enzyme content. An example will clarify my reasons for thinking this. Human cells are capable of forming an enzyme called "synthase" that synthesizes the amino acid glutamine. However, certain strains of human cells form different amounts of the synthase enzyme under differing conditions. If glutamine is absent from the culture medium, the enzyme is formed at a maximal rate. If it is present, even in concentrations as low as two parts per million, the enzyme is formed at one fifteenth of the maximal rate, although the cells grow perfectly normally (18). This is an indication of the sensitive response of some control schemes to chemical stimuli from the environment. It is also another example of the many parallelisms that occur in the results of work with microbes and with human cells, for it was first shown with bacteria that the product of an enzymatically catalyzed reaction might repress the formation of the enzyme involved. This general mode of regulation is called "feedback" and is of the sort one would expect to find operating in biological systems. It is encouraging that it has turned up more than once in work with cultured human cells.

One additional point worth mentioning is that in some strains of human cells, formation of the synthase enzyme is not sensitive to the repressive influence of glutamine in the medium. Therefore, hereditary variation involving the control scheme has already turned up, too. Finally, the synthase enzyme is not ubiquitously distributed in the cells of the intact vertebrate body. Instead, it occurs in largest amounts in the liver and central nervous system. Studies with chick embryos have shown that the rate at which this enzyme is formed in the brain changes sharply at a definite stage of development (19). Does the control scheme discovered in cultured cells have real relevance to the control over enzyme production in the embryo? This question points to one of the directions of future work with cultured cells.

Let us turn now to another fascinating, recently discovered aspect of control over gene expression in mammalian cells. It concerns a hypothesis about the X chromosome that can be stated in two parts (20, 21):

1. The cells of female mammals have two X chromosomes but the genes of only one X function in any individual cell.
2. Decisions are made during embryonic development as to which X will function and which will not. The decision, once made, is fixed. That is, functional X chromosomes produce replicas that also function in later generations of cells, and nonfunctional chromosomes produce replicas that do not function. Finally, the initial decisions as to which of the two X chromosomes will function occur at random among the cells.

The hypothesis has predictable consequences that we can examine. It says that the effective dosage of some genes on the X chromosome is the same in males and females, creating a parity between the sexes regarding the quantitative expression of genes not concerned with the determination of sex. This sort of equalization seems to be achieved in man.

The genetic determinants for the production of the enzyme glucose-6-phosphate dehydrogenase are on the X chromosome. The activity of this enzyme in the red blood cells of human beings does not vary with the number of X chromosomes per cell, whether that number be one, two, three, or four. Such individuals with abnormal numbers of X chromosomes may also result from the process of nondisjunction that has already been shown to affect several autosomes (13, 14). The same comment applies to cells cultured from the skin of such individuals. This lack of proportionality between gene dosage and gene expression could be achieved in several ways, but we have a good clue for sorting out the possibilities in a microscopically visible feature of human cells. This is the sex chromatin body, which appears to be an X chromosome that is wholly or mainly condensed when the other chromosomes are not, i.e., during the period called interphase that separates successive cell divisions (22) (Plate 7). Its condensed state causes it to

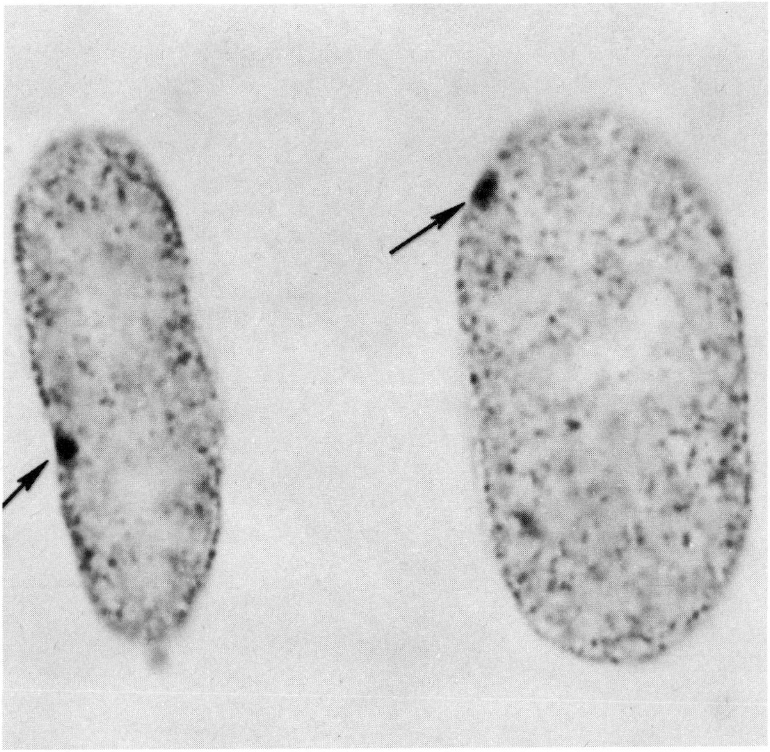

PLATE 7. The interphase nuclei of two cells cultivated from the skin of a human female, magnified about 3500-fold. A stain (Feulgen) reacting specifically with the DNA of the chromosomes in the nuclei was used, and the cytoplasms of the cells are not visible. Each nucleus has a single sex chromatin body (*arrows*) formed by condensation of one of its two X chromosomes. Some genes on the condensed X chromosomes are not expressed (see page 70). The cells of males have only one X chromosome, and it does not form a sex chromatin body.

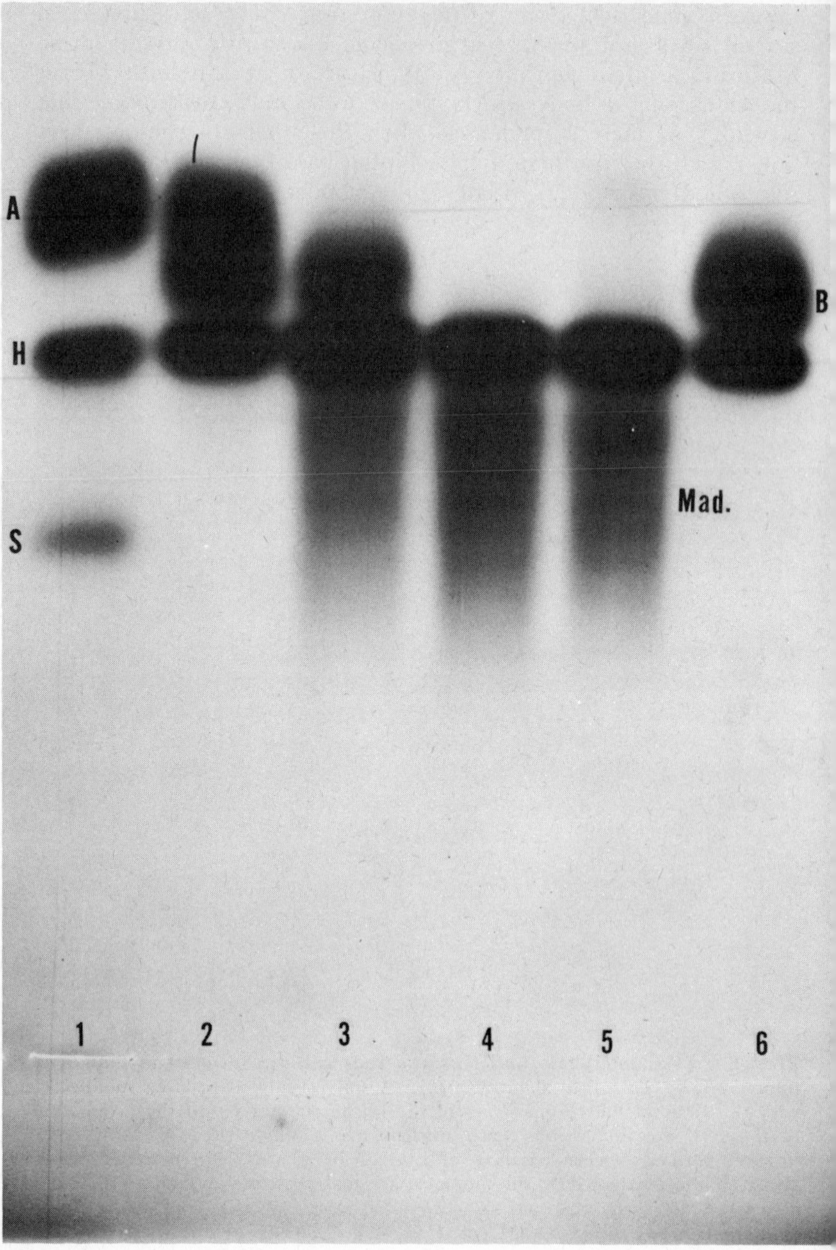
A
H
S
B
Mad.
1
2
3
4
5
6

stain intensely with certain dyes that interact with chromosomes while the other chromosomes are so extended and slender as to be individually invisible. There are reasons to believe that genes of the chromosomes, in general, are not active when they are condensed, functioning only when they are extended. Sex chromatin bodies are found only in cells having more than one X, the general rule being that the number of sex chromatin bodies per cell is one less than the total number of X chromosomes. If we identify condensed X's with the chromosomes that do not function, then the quantitative relation between the number of sex chromatin bodies and the number of X chromosomes explains the lack of proportionality between enzyme activity and X chromosomes that was just described. It is noteworthy that the formation of a sex chromatin body is a persistent feature of cells cultivated from the skin of females.

PLATE 8. Photograph of a starch gel showing three different varieties of the enzyme glucose-6-phosphate dehydrogenase (G6PD) found in man. (This gel and photograph were prepared in collaboration with Dr. Walter E. Nance of Vanderbilt University. The photograph is slightly larger than life size.) Red blood cells of each suitable individual were disrupted, and a drop of each person's hemolysate was placed in a separate slot near one end of a thin slab of a gelled starch solution. An electric current was passed through the gel causing the electrically charged enzyme molecules to migrate. Proteins of differing size or electric charge migrate through such gels with differing speeds.

The G6PD enzymes were located in this gel by overlaying it with substances that formed an insoluble, purple precipitate wherever the enzymes acted on them. Where G6PD was absent, the gel remained colorless.

The dark bands found at *H* in all six individuals were formed by hemoglobin, which serves as a convenient reference. Individual number 1 also had a mutant form of hemoglobin at *S*.

Type B of G6PD is the commonest variety of the enzyme. It migrates slightly faster than hemoglobin in the type of gel used here and is the only type of G6PD detected in the red cells of individual number 6.

Type A is the second commonest variety of G6PD and migrates slightly faster than type B. It is the only type found in the red cells of individual number 1. A third type of G6PD shown here migrates more slowly than hemoglobin and less compactly, forming a smear. It is called G6PD-Mad., for Madison.

The variants of G6PD illustrated here are also produced in the fibroblastic cells cultured from the skins of the individuals whose red blood cells were used. Individuals number 2 and 3 were females, producing two different types of G6PD. Number 2 had a gene for the production of type A on one X chromosome and a gene for type B on the other X. That is, she was heterozygous for genes A and B. Similarly, number 3 was heterozygous for genes B and Mad. Single cells derived from her skin formed clones that produced only type B enzyme or type Mad. enzyme, but not both. (See pages 70-74.)

A second consequence of the hypothesis follows from the presumed stability of the differentiation between the two X's from one cell generation to the next. Consider two different versions, A and B, of the same kind of gene, A being located on one of the X chromosomes and B on the other. The hypothesis says that in some cell lineages the chromosome bearing gene A is nonfunctional and only gene B is expressed, while in other cell lineages of the same individual the roles of the X's are the opposite. The point is that no cell acts as if *both* A and B were functional, although both types of genetic material are present.

The cultured human cell has turned out to be the best available material for investigating the validity of this prediction. The first requirement is two different versions of a gene of the X chromosome. Mutations in the determinants that produce glucose-6-phosphate dehydrogenase alter the speed with which the extracted enzyme molecules in solution migrate under the influence of an electric current (23, 24). At least six different varieties of this sort are known and we might refer to one of them as "A" and a second one as "B." The requirement just mentioned is filled by locating females who produce both A and B varieties of the enzyme. Such females are easily detected by testing the enzyme extracted from their red blood cells (Plate 8). Populations of cells cultured from the skin of such individuals also exhibit both varieties of the enzyme. The problem now is to isolate single cells from the population and have them produce enough progeny to permit testing for the types of enzyme present. If the hypothesis is correct, then such clonal populations should exhibit only the A variety or only the B, but not both. Of course, one might argue that the presence of only one variety of enzyme could be due to the loss of one of the X chromosomes during the process of producing the populations from single cells. But this question can be answered by examination of the chromosomes of the cells. Since the draft of this paper was prepared, the hypothesis of the single-active-X discussed here has been put to the test in two laboratories working with cultured human cells, and in exactly the manner described in the preceding paragraph. Both laboratories have obtained very similar results that confirm the hypothesis (25, 26) clearing the way for use of the cultivated cells in ferreting out the underlying basis for the differences in behavior of the active and inactive X chromosomes.

I have given so much attention to this particular problem for a number of reasons. It involves an extremely interesting example of control over chromosome behavior and gene expression. Furthermore, it has such distinctive features that one suspects it of being one of those interesting differences in genetic behavior between human cells and bacteria that one should be alert to. Finally, the outline of the attack on the problem encompasses almost all the manipulative advantages I ascribed to the cultured human cells at the beginning of my presentation. It demonstrates how these advantages can be turned to account in tackling new and interesting problems in human heredity.

Cultures of cells will be a necessary tool for those who would develop and test techniques for altering man's hereditary makeup. We can imagine two humane objectives in applying such techniques. One of these would be to provide the body with enough appropriately modified somatic cells to improve the performance of an individual afflicted with genetically engendered malfunction. The other would be improvement in the genetic content of an individual's reproductive cells, in this way hopefully improving the performance of his progeny. The techniques actually or prospectively available for modifying the heredity of microorganisms have already been masterfully presented by Drs. Luria and Tatum. One need only mention that efforts to apply many of them to work with cultured cells have already been initiated. The reader of this book can readily anticipate some of the problems that would be encountered in the use of such techniques on cells that reside in human bodies rather than in laboratory culture vessels and that many of these problems will be the same whether somatic cells or reproductive cells are dealt with. Some of them arise from the usually low numerical efficiency with which present techniques effect any particular kind of genetic change. This requires that the initially small populations of altered cells in the body be built up to levels where they become effective in providing improved function. The problem is easily and effectively solved in work with cultures by the application of selective procedures, which sacrifice the great majority of cells in permitting growth of a few special ones. These procedures might so disrupt intact individuals as to limit their applications in work with human beings. A possible way of hurdling this obstacle would be to isolate cells from the body, alter them and carry out selection in culture, and then implant large populations of altered cells back in the body. This procedure may not be as far-fetched as it seems but it does illustrate the sort of virtuoso techniques that might have to be devised.

Situations where selection cannot be applied at all come to mind, for effective selection demands increase in cell number. Some genetic diseases are expressed in organs such as the liver, pancreas, and central nervous system. Cells in these organs multiply at a very low rate in the body, if at all, and very quickly stop multiplying in culture, barring any obvious application of selective techniques following genetic alteration. In fact, certain chemical agents for effecting genetic changes might not be effective in such cells since their action depends on the replication of DNA. Even large increases in the efficiency of inducing alterations in genetic material would not necessarily eliminate the need for selection unless they were accompanied by improved control over the types of changes that occur. Otherwise, desired alterations might often be accompanied by undesirable ones. Some of these interrelated difficulties might be overcome by inducing genetic changes in the organ rudiments of embryos, including embryonic reproductive cells, where cell proliferation occurs at a rapid rate. This might permit the necessary increase in the population of altered cells but would also demand very fine control over all aspects of the procedure in order to ensure normal development of the embryo.

This sketch of some of the technical obstacles hindering the repair or replacement of faulty genetic material has applied to somatic cells in situ because of their obvious analogy to the somatic cells cultured in vitro. But the related obstacles of inefficient induction of genetic change, poor control over the specific nature of the changes that *are* induced, and impediments to the free use of selection for desirably altered types of cells would bedevil attempts to modify reproductive cells, as well.

It should also be clear by now that the types of traits that can be studied and subjected to alteration in culture are expressed by and definable in terms of single cells and, often, single genetic determinants. The study of human heredity with individuals has dealt at least as much with traits that can be defined only in terms of aggregates of cells, interactions between different cell types, and multiple genetic determinants. The techniques for genetic alteration that are available now seem poorly adapted to modifying undesired expression of these traits, and yet it is the modification of just such traits that in many cases would make the ability to control human heredity worthwhile. This distinction is made in greater detail by Dr. Muller but it is meaningful to make it here in order to place the work with cultured cells in its proper perspective.

The successful application, to human cells, of the kinds of techniques that genetically alter microbes is likely to mean alteration of those cells, perhaps a gene at a time and with regard to traits that are simply defined and expressed. This is far from being the total aim of an effort to improve man's hereditary makeup. Nevertheless, repair work on human genetic material can take its proper place in a battery of techniques designed for easing the weight of man's burden of deleterious genes. It would be foolish to think that the problems met with in extrapolating microbial genetic techniques to work with human cells will forever remain unsolved. The scope and speed of work on human heredity and cultured cells have increased greatly. In the seven-month interval between the writing of the first and final drafts of this paper it was possible for the author and co-workers to discover a completely new form of human glucose-6-phosphate dehydrogenase, confirm the location of the mutant gene on the X chromosome by family studies, establish cultures of cells from suitable donors, and execute a complete test of the single-active-X hypothesis with the cultured cells. In this same interval two other variants of the enzyme were described by others, as were variants of lactic acid dehydrogenase and 6-phosphogluconic dehydrogenase. All of these are mutations that are likely to be expressed in cultured cells, increasing their usefulness for genetic analysis. This brings me to my final point. I have tried to show how cultures of human cells will help us to gain knowledge *about* genetics. This is knowledge about ourselves, and it is desirable that we have it.

References

This list of references is not a complete one but indicates only some of the review or special articles that exemplify the point dealt with in the text.

1. I. Lieberman and P. Ove, Estimation of mutation rates with mammalian cells in culture. *Proc. Nat. Acad. Sci. U.S.A.,* **45**:872, 1959.
2. W. Szybalski, Genetics of human cell lines, II. Method for determination of mutation rates to drug resistance. *Exp. Cell Res.,* **18**:588, 1959.
3. T. T. Puck, The action of radiation on mammalian cells. *Amer. Naturalist,* **94**:95, 1960.
4. M. M. Elkind and H. Sutton, Postirradiation survival kinetics of mammalian cells grown in culture. *J. Cell. Comp. Physiol.* (*Supp.*), **58**:113, 1961.
5. E. H. Szybalska and W. Szybalski, Genetics of human cell lines, IV. DNA-mediated heritable transformation of a biochemical trait. *Proc. Nat. Acad. Sci. U.S.A.,* **48**:2026, 1962.
6. H. Temin, Malignant transformation in cell cultures. *Health Lab. Sci.,* **1**:79, April 1964.

7. H. M. Shein and J. F. Enders, Transformation induced by Simian virus 40 in human renal cell cultures, I. Morphology and growth characteristics. *Proc. Nat. Acad. Sci. U.S.A.,* **48**:1164 and 1350, 1962.
8. W. W. Nichols, A. Levan, G. Hall, and G. Östergren, Measles-associated chromosome breakage. *Hereditas* (*Lund*), **48**:367, 1962.
9. G. Barski, S. Sorieul, and Fr. Cornefert, "Hybrid" type cells in combined cultures of two different mammalian cell strains. *J. Nat. Cancer Inst.,* **26**:1269, 1961.
10. B. Ephrussi and S. Sorieul, Mating of somatic cells *in vitro. Univ. Mich. Med. Bull.,* **28**:347, 1962.
11. E. H. Y. Chu and N. H. Giles, Comparative chromosomal studies on mammalian cells in culture, I. The HeLa strain and its mutant clonal derivatives. *J. Nat. Cancer Inst.,* **20**:383, 1957.
12. M. Vogt, A study of the relationship between karyotype and phenotype in cloned lines of strain HeLa. *Genetics,* **44**:1257, 1959.
13. J. Lejeune, The 21 trisomy-current stage of chromosomal research, in: *Progress in Medical Genetics* (A. Steinberg and A. Bearn, eds.), vol. 3, p. 144. Grune and Stratton Publishers, New York, 1964.
14. D. W. Smith, The no. 18 trisomy and D_1 trisomy syndromes. *Pediat. Clin. N. Amer.,* **10**:389, 1963.
15. H. Harris, *Human Biochemical Genetics.* Cambridge University Press, London and New York, 1959.
16. R. S. Krooth and A. N. Weinberg, Studies on cell lines developed from the tissues of patients with galactosemia. *J. Exp. Med.,* **133**:1155, 1961.
17. L. A. Herzenberg, Steps toward a genetics of somatic cells in culture. *J. Cell. Comp. Physiol.* (Suppl.), **60**:145, 1962.
18. R. DeMars, The inhibition by glutamine of glutamyl transferase formation in cultures of human cells. *Biochim. Biophys. Acta,* **27**:435, 1957.
19. D. Rudnick and H. Waelsch, Development of glutamotransferase in the nervous system of the chick, in: *Biochemistry of the Developing Nervous System* (H. Welch, ed.), p. 335. Academic Press, Inc., New York, 1955.
20. M. F. Lyon, Sex chromatin and gene action in the mammalian X-chromosome. *Am. J. Hum. Genet.,* **14**:135, 1962.
21. L. B. Russell, Mammalian X-chromosome action: Inactivation limited in spread and region of origin. *Science,* **140**:976, 1963.
22. Symposium on sex chromatin. *Acta Cytol.* (*Phila.*), **6**:1, 1962.
23. S. H. Boyer, I. H. Porter, and R. G. Weilbacker, Electrophoretic heterogeneity of glucose-6-phosphate dehydrogenase and its relationship to enzyme deficiency in man. *Proc. Nat. Acad. Sci. U.S.A.,* **48**:1868, 1962.
24. H. N. Kirkman and E. M. Hendrickson, Sex-linked electrophoretic difference in glucose-6-phosphate dehydrogenase. *Am. J. Hum. Genet.,* **15**:241, 1963.

25. R. G. Davidson, H. M. Nitowski, and B. Childs, Demonstration of two populations of cells in the human female heterozygous for glucose-6-phosphate dehydrogenase variants. *Proc. Nat. Acad. Sci. U.S.A.,* **50**:481, 1963.
26. R. DeMars and W. E. Nance, Electrophoretic variants of glucose-6-phosphate dehydrogenase and the single-active-X in cultivated human cells. *J. Cell. Comp. Physiol.,* 1964 (in press).
27. This final reference is a fairly current and diversified collection of articles that describes many facets of the work being done in the field discussed in this paper.
    Approaches to the genetic analysis of mammalian cells. *Univ. Mich. Med. Bull.,* **28**:265, 1962.

CHAPTER 4

Prospects for Genetic Analysis in Man

G. Pontecorvo, Department of Genetics
The University, Glasgow

Up to a few years ago we could have taken a balanced view of our gross ignorance of human genetics. No doubt this ignorance—which still persists today in spite of minor advances—was intellectually regrettable. But man's large measure of control over the outside world, and over his own biological shortcomings—for instance by using insulin to combat diabetes and clothing to compensate for the lack of natural protection—made a profound knowledge of genetics not essential for progress. In other words, good "nurture" in the broadest sense of good control of physical and social conditions from conception to old age, and good medicine, were incomparably more fruitful than good eugenics. The advances in the physical and medical well-being of a substantial part of mankind in the last 50 years bear out this conclusion.

In this chapter I shall consider, among other things, whether an unconcerned attitude about our ignorance of human genetics is still justified in the face of the present rate of scientific and technological progress. The biology of man, and in particular the hereditary constitution that underlies it, is the result of a gradual process of evolution the pace of which is appreciable only over millions of years. The change in the outside world produced by man himself in the last 100 years has been greater than in all the previous millions of years of evolution of the mammals. Thus, our biology is faced by something of which it has had no previous experience.

We may well have to take a deliberate hand in speeding its change. This is a purely negative aspect of the challenge. The positive aspect is that on social, ethical, and other grounds we may decide that, given the means of doing so, we want to take a hand consciously in moulding human nature, irrespective of any necessity for mere survival. It is generally agreed among biologists that the means of doing so in a very minor way have already been available and in use for some time, but that it is reasonable to expect developments of these means on a colossal scale. Where opinions differ is in the time required.

I am not dealing here with the philosophy or the ethics of this task, when it becomes inevitable or desirable. First of all, I am not more competent than any other man in the street. Second, present-day philosophies, systems of ethics and religions—no doubt evolved in part as an element in and of the biological evolution of man—are unprepared for, and possibly unable to cope with, situations continuously changing at an unprecedented pace. The best that we as biologists, with our specialized knowledge, can do is to try to clarify the biological problems and the technical possibilities, and make them part of the common knowledge.

The hope is that widespread information and rational discussion may ultimately lead to philosophical, ethical, and social preparedness for the moment when the changes in the world at large, and the advances in our knowledge of human biology, will have made it necessary or desirable to take deliberate action on an unprecedented scale.

But it would be a delusion to think that, even under the almost utopian conditions of education and general consent just suggested, action to modify human nature deliberately—in short "human engineering"—other than applied to informed and consenting adults, may not involve some form of individual restraint; hence the necessity to start thinking now about what is coming.

Human Engineering

Human engineering in one form or another has, of course, been practiced on a minor scale for a long time. Prenatal care, immunization, blood transfusion, organ transplantation, plastic surgery, supplementation (sometimes compulsory) of the diet are all practices of human engineering that we have taken in our stride. Even the tragic accident with thalidomide has passed as one of the occasional failures in the applications of biological knowledge, due to the fact that that knowledge can never be complete.

Implementation of all these minor steps in human engineering has not aroused any profound emotional resistance, nor, by and large, has it produced any acute awareness that important ethical and social principles were involved. The inclusion of iodine in the normal diet of people living in certain mountainous areas of Europe has raised the average level of intelligence in those areas by a very considerable extent. Cod-liver oil given to expectant mothers and children in a smoky town like Glasgow has improved to an obvious extent the physique of the population, and insulin has kept in active life millions of otherwise genetically doomed persons. These are examples of the simplest kinds of human engineering affecting mental and physical features, respectively. We take for granted action of this kind.

Yet, the ethical and social issues raised by these past feats of human engineering are qualitatively no different from those we shall have to face in the future. The difference will be quantitative: in scale and rate. Even so, the individual steps may still go on being so small that none of them singly will bring those issues forcibly to light: but the sum total is likely to be tremendous. That is why we have to look for those issues now, identify them, state them clearly, and make them a matter of universal knowledge. Only this way can we hope to develop ethical standards by democratic means and draw the necessary social conclusions. The alternative is a wise oligarchy knowing and doing what they think good for the rest in the way so vividly pictured by Aldous Huxley 40 years ago in *Brave New World*.

The analogy between the position in biology now and the position in physics about 1935 has been mentioned repeatedly, also in the present book. The analogy is not quite correct. By about 1935 the release of nuclear energy was theoretically certain. What was very doubtful in the minds of practically all physicists was whether it would ever have any practical interest at all. Because of this uncertainty, and the then-prevailing idea that scientists should mind their own business, physicists did next to nothing to inform society of what might come. When they realized that practical applications were only a matter of effort, the war was on and, with it, secrecy. The result was that the momentous decisions, first of making the bomb and then of dropping it, were made by a handful of men inevitably not expressing public opinion on this matter. Even if the public could have been consulted, it could not have made any rational contribution because there had not been any ethical and intellectual preparation.

In biology today the position is almost the reverse. On the one hand we are convinced that, one way or another, profound advances in the technology of human engineering are going to come and could be speeded up by adequate concentration of effort. On the other hand, we have no theoretical grounds for predicting which particular approaches—out of the many possible—are more likely to be workable. Finally, biologists, and in general all scientists, today have learned from the experience of nuclear energy and are conscious that it is their duty to inform society of the implications of the advances in their own fields.

There are, obviously, two conceivable main lines of approach in human engineering. Suppose we wished to improve a type of automobile. We could do so by putting a new blueprint into production. We could also do it by keeping an old blueprint but intervening at one or more points in the production line and somewhat altering the operations at those points. In human engineering the analogy is modification of heredity or modification of development: we use the old term "eugenics" for improvement via heredity and the new term, coined by Lederberg, "euphenics" for improvement via development. The two procedures are, of course, interrelated to a considerable extent.

The Need for Knowledge in Human Genetics

As mentioned previously, in the last few tens of thousands of years human biology has uniquely evolved more by "euphenic" than by "eugenic" procedures, both largely unconscious or at least unplanned. We may well wonder whether this is going to continue, with the difference that action will become increasingly more deliberate and on a much larger scale. If this is so, however, we should be no less interested in advancing the knowledge of an area of human biology in which it is pitifully inadequate: human genetics.

Going back to the analogy of the automobile, we need a very thorough knowledge of the blueprint so that our interventions at one or another point of the production line may be efficiently chosen and applied. Perhaps an architectural analogy is useful: many of us have had the experience of trying to introduce changes into a building during its construction. Without a detailed knowledge of the architect's plans it could be difficult to change even the position of a door. In the same way, most euphenic interventions aimed at modifying in desired directions one or more developmental processes in the immature individual are likely to require precise knowledge at least of some part of the blueprint of the individual himself, i.e., of his heredity.

Thus, even if advances in the *practice* of human engineering were to continue almost exclusively along the euphenic direction, parallel radical advances in the *knowledge* of human genetics are obviously indispensable. Clearly, any one type of euphenic intervention—for instance the hypothetical use of a hormone to affect the development of the growing brain—may be applicable or not, or more or less efficiently applicable according to the heredity of each individual. This might raise the purely diagnostic problem of identifying the relevant hereditary constitution of each fetus, or newborn, in order to decide on the advisability and kind of treatment.

As human engineering practices advance, however, even if they go on relying essentially on euphenic interventions, we may reach a time when modifications of heredity may become advisable in order that euphenic treatments need no longer be limited to, or effective in, only a fraction of the individuals of a population.

Other chapters in this book have dealt with the prospects of deliberate *control* of the genetic constitution of the individual. My subject here is the much lighter one—yet still formidable—of the prospects and limitations of the *analysis* of the genetic constitution of the individual. The huge difference between the two tasks is like that between being able to describe something—admittedly very complicated—and being able to modify it in a particular way.

Genetic Analysis in Man

The reasons why genetic analysis has advanced so slowly in man are well known. Up to recent times genetic analysis in any organism was possible only by means of the classification of the different kinds and proportions of germ cells produced by an individual. This classification was usually indirect, i.e., based on the proportions of the progeny with different characters arising from those germ cells. In other words, genetic analysis required the results of sexual reproduction and large numbers of progeny. In an organism like man, in which the time between generations is over 20 years, the number of progeny per pair is extremely small, and there is no possibility of experimental breeding, progress was necessarily almost impossible.

This is no longer true. The developments in genetics of the last decade, especially the developments in the genetics of microorganisms, have made it clear that genetic analysis is not necessarily limited to the use of the results of sexual reproduction. Furthermore, the birth and the spectacular successes of molecular genetics have tremendously simplified the ways of looking at most of the phenomena of heredity by regarding them as by-products of variations in the synthesis and activities of nucleic acids and proteins.

As a consequence of the changes in basic knowledge, the prospects for genetic analysis in man are now quite different. It is true that we are still groping with the initial spadework, and in no way has there been—as yet—a breakthrough. But there is a sufficiently varied array of obvious lines of attack to justify sober optimism. I shall illustrate briefly some of these lines, under two main headings: (1) genetic analysis via recombination in somatic cells, and (2) genetic analysis via "hybridization" between segments of the genetic material (DNA) and their primary products (RNA).

Genetic analysis via recombination in somatic cells. This heading includes all the extensions to somatic cells of the principles of classical genetic analysis which were in the past applicable only to the processes of formation of the germ cells. Among the techniques that conceivably may be applied are all those based on the novel mechanisms of recombination that have come to light, or have been clarified, in microorganisms: i.e., *transduction,* the virus-mediated transfer from one cell to another of genetic material; *transformation,* the incorporation into the genetic material, the DNA, of a cell of a segment of DNA from another cell; and *somatic segregation,* the production by a cell of daughter cells containing its genetic material variously reassorted.

For genetic analysis, it is conceivable to use somatic recombination resulting from any one of the three mechanisms just mentioned, either directly on the somatic cells in the body or on somatic cells in culture. In both cases the aim is to identify the rare cells that have properties different from the rest as a consequence of any one of the processes of somatic recombination. While the use of all three processes of recombination mentioned—transduction, transformation, and somatic segregation—can, in principle, be attempted with somatic cells in culture, in the case of somatic cells in the body, we cannot, of course, experiment and we can only rely on rare processes of segregation occurring spontaneously and giving origin to mosaic tissues. For this reason there is a much wider scope in the use of cultured cells than in the search for mosaics in body tissues.

In what does genetic analysis via somatic cells consist, and what are the difficulties? Consider two genes, hypothetically known to be on the same chromosome pair, and two alternative forms—two allelomorphs—of one determining the presence or absence of a particular antigen, respectively, and two allelomorphs of the other gene determining two different forms, A and B, of the enzyme 6-phospho-gluconate dehydrogenase (6PGD), respectively. Suppose we were able to recognize at the cellular level in cultured cells the two pairs of alternative properties (my colleague Dr. Renwick informs me that this is so in the case of 6PGD). Then we could establish a culture of skin cells from an individual who inherited from one parent the allelomorphs for, say, the production of the antigen and the production of (A)6PGD, and from the other parent the allelomorphs for the absence of the antigen and the production of (B)6PGD. We might then find that the cultured cells occasionally produce variants ("segregants"), which differ from the bulk of the population in showing either the A or the B form of 6PGD, but not both. Among these rare segregants we would then look for what has happened in respect to the other pair of alternatives (presence or absence of the antigen). We would find certain characteristic associations from the proportions of which we might be able to conclude, if we did not know it already, that the two genes are on the same chromosome pair and even that, in conventional units, they are so much apart.

The aim of formal genetic analysis, in man as in any other organism, is precisely the identification of the genes, their allocation to chromosome pairs, and the description of their sequence along each chromosome pair.

In principle, genetic analysis via somatic cells could give the same kind of answers that once required the results of sexual reproduction. In lieu of waiting for somatic segregation—as exemplified hypothetically—it is conceivable that we could speed it up considerably, for instance by the use of *p*-fluorophenylalanine (which is extremely effective to this end in lower organisms) or colchicine. Furthermore, in cultured cells this kind of analysis could be based on the use of processes of recombination other than spontaneous or induced somatic segregation: for instance, transduction or transformation if they turn out to be feasible in human cells in respect to characters known to be under gene control.

I hasten to point out that genetic analysis via recombination in somatic cells has been in the programs of a few laboratories in various parts of the world for about five years. Nowhere, as far as I know, has there been a clear-cut result, though the results obtained with mouse tumors in Dr. Klein's laboratory seem to come very near to this. Also, in Dr. Ephrussi's laboratory, conclusive evidence was obtained that whole chromosomes undergo segregation in cultures of mouse cells. The difficulties have been of two main kinds. To put it crudely: too few "markers" and too many regulatory genes.

By "markers" I mean differences known to be genetically determined between individuals, which are recognizable at the cellular level and persist in cultures of cells from those individuals. Dr. DeMars has enumerated three of the five markers so far identified as usable in human cell cultures. The five are: acatalasia, galactosemia, G6PD deficiency, G6PD variation, and 6PGD variation. Why are such small numbers of cellular markers known when there are so many genetically determined differences between individual human beings? The present views on gene action in differentiated tissues give a clue.

Practically all types of cell of the body are supposed to carry the same endowment of genes, but in any one type of cell only a fraction of all genes is active. If, in a certain type of cell—say skin fibroblasts—a gene is inactive, obviously we cannot distinguish, in respect to the relevant property, between skin fibroblasts from an individual carrying a particular allele of that gene and skin fibroblasts from another individual carrying a different allele. For instance, liver cells of normal individuals produce the enzyme phenylalanine hydroxylase, which is absent from liver cells of phenylpyruvic imbeciles, and this difference is known to be genetically determined. Skin cells of both normal persons and imbeciles lack the enzyme. Clearly, we cannot make use of that enzymatic difference as a marker in cultures of skin cells—the most convenient type of human cell for culture—unless we find a way of persuading the cultured skin cells from normal individuals to produce the enzyme.

Another related aspect of this difficulty is that a particular gene may be active in a tissue and yet when cells of that tissue are cultured the activity is lost. This is, for instance, the case for the A and B blood group antigens: although present in a proportion of skin cells, they are lost in cultures established from skin.

A further aspect is, in a sense, the reverse. For instance, alkaline phosphatase is almost absent from healthy skin cells. Cells in cultures established from skin are also almost negative, but it is possible to induce high alkaline phosphatase activity in them by growing them under special conditions, for example by supplementing the culture medium with organic monophosphate. When we do this we can compare cultures of skin cells from different individuals and we then find that they differ in their response to the inducer. Though in this case we do not yet know whether these differences at the cell culture level are an expression of the genetic constitutions of the individuals from whom the cells were derived, clearly there is an important lesson to learn here.

The general deduction is that in an organism as complex as man, a high proportion (my guess is the overwhelming proportion) of all genes is concerned with intracellular, or even intranuclear, regulatory processes. In particular, many determine at which rate and under which cellular, histological, humoral, and external conditions other genes—"structural" genes, which carry the information for the synthesis of proteins—can work.

This means that in the spadework for the search for cellular markers, we shall have to put a major effort into the discovery for each "structural" gene of the cultural conditions permitting its expression. This, in its turn, will make it possible to analyze the large proportion of the genetic material that controls regulatory processes.

In conclusion, genetic analysis via recombination in somatic cells is still at the stage of possibility, though of an extremely promising one.

Genetic analysis via "hybridization" between DNA and RNA. A technique of immense potentiality has been developed in the last two years. The chemical means came from Dr. Doty's laboratory, and they have been put to good use for genetic analysis in Dr. Spiegelman's laboratory. The essentials are that DNA is separated into its two single-strand components by heating. Sections of the single-stranded DNA will anneal (hybridize) specifically with sections of RNA of complementary base sequence. We must remember that the primary products of gene activity are supposed to be RNA with base sequence complementary to DNA: these include messenger RNA, repressor RNA, sRNA, or ribosomal RNA, as may be the case. The RNA artificially combined with single-stranded DNA is not broken down by RNA-ase, and therefore hybridization can be used to purify such RNA from the rest. The opposite purification, that of DNA by elimination of the fraction that is not combined with complementary RNA, has not yet been achieved, but it is not far away. When both are possible we shall have a means of isolating individual genes (DNA) by combining them with their immediate products (RNA), and vice versa.

Clearly this is a completely novel method of genetic analysis, and I for one have no doubt that it will eventually become a main tool—possibly the main tool—in genetics. However, this is for the future. With organisms more complex than bacteria and viruses, there are still serious preliminary troubles, but they do not seem to be major stumbling blocks.

Dr. Luria has stressed in his chapter that directed specific mutation, i.e., mutation of a particular gene in a determined way, is likely to require specific mutagens as complex as the genes themselves. It is clear that the technique of isolation of individual genes and their individual RNA products just mentioned will supply a firm steppingstone for the production of specific mutagens.

Conclusions

We come thus to the general picture that decisive advances in the genetic analysis of man are likely to come, on the one hand, from the use of recombination in cultures of somatic cells and, on the other hand, from the use of DNA-RNA hybridization, the latter both in cultured cells and in fresh somatic cells (blood, sperm, etc.).

A knowledge of human genetics far greater than the impressive knowledge we already have of, say, the genetics of bacteriophage T4 is required for rational human engineering, be it of the eugenic or of the euphenic type. How big this task is can be gauged from a few figures. Bacteriophage T4—an organism about 1/250,000th of an inch long—has a total genetic material (DNA) 200,000 nucleotide pairs long. The total number of genes of bacteriophage T4 is of the order of 100. Of these, some 20 have already been identified and located, and in the case of four of them, fine structure analysis is fairly advanced.

In man, the total DNA is of the order of 1000 million nucleotide pairs. On the basis of various rather arbitrary assumptions, the total number of genes is guessed as between 50,000 and 1 million. Of these, some 100 have been identified, but only a few have been crudely located, and none has been analyzed in its fine structure. Even when techniques of recombination analysis and of DNA-RNA hybridization as simple as those used for bacteriophage will be applied to human cells, the task of analyzing the genetics of man will still be prodigious. But the task of using the knowledge so gained to control human heredity will be incomparably more so.

Still, we have to consider the possibilities, and the courageous initiative of Ohio Wesleyan University in bringing these matters into the open can only be admired.

Discussion—Part II

Dr. Szybalski

Throughout this book the recurrent theme has been engineering—molecular engineering, human engineering, euphenic engineering—even if not always so expressed. Since I may be the only one on this panel with a bona fide degree in engineering, I would like to comment briefly on the subject. Of course I consider engineering very important; after all, it was once my primary field of interest. As in other fields of human technological endeavor, I trust that the "know-how" of this discipline should permit efficient translation of relatively simple discoveries in molecular genetics into the very complicated field of clinical bioengineering. But this translation process is often a very complicated one and based on many interdisciplinary approaches, characteristic for the engineering sciences. I would like to discuss one example of such an attempt to translate a simple biological observation into something useful from the clinical point of view. I have chosen the radiosensitization of 5-halodeoxyuridine-labeled cells, since it pertains to the chemistry of DNA, a primary bearer of heredity, and since I have some first-hand experience in this field.

It has been shown in several laboratories, including that of Dr. S. Zamenhof, that several halogenated analogues of thymidine, including 5-chloro-, 5-bromo-, 5-iodo-, and 5-trifluoromethyl deoxyuridine, can be incorporated into the DNA of a variety of cell species, including the DNA of human cells, the latter studied in our laboratory. The following observations were made with human cells grown in the presence of 5-bromo- or 5-iododeoxyuridine: (1) only cells in which DNA is replicating incorporate the halogenated analogues, (2) the cells are not killed by analogue incorporation into their DNA, and (3) the analogue-labeled cells become more sensitive to radiation. These observations suggested an obvious practical clinical application: selective sensitization of localized tumors to x-ray therapy. The sensitization should be selective because only cells synthesizing DNA, i.e., primarily replicating cancer cells, would incorporate the analogue.

This approach worked very nicely with cancer-like cells grown in tissue culture, but as soon as it was extended to animal tumors or to clinical cases of human cancer, many difficulties became at once apparent. Let me discuss them one by one.

1. It is easy to establish a constant and well-defined concentration of the analogue in the in vitro system (closed system) where the cells are simply submerged in the analogue-containing medium. The in vivo system is an open one with the drug being rapidly excreted unless some means of controlling the drug excretion or its constant infusion are provided. The drug concentration is not constant, with rapidly changing concentration gradients throughout the whole body.

2. Another problem encountered only in vivo is the rapid catabolic destruction of the halogenated analogue (dehalogenation, sugar-base cleavage), which process is carried on mainly by the liver. Bypassing the liver, chemical modification of the halogenated analogue, and inhibition of this catabolic liver function are potential means of restoring the efficacy of the thymidine analogues. Another way is to develop new drugs that would specifically inhibit the enzymes involved in the destruction of the halogenated analogues.

3. Besides tumor there are many other actively dividing tissues in the animal or human body, including bone marrow and intestinal epithelium. These would have to be bypassed during infusion of the drug. Incorporation of thymidine analogues could also be counteracted by peripheral administration of thymidine. If these tissues, however, were located far enough from the tumor, their radiosensitization by analogue incorporation would be of minor importance, since the x-ray beam could be directed only at the tumor.

4. General or specific toxicity directed at some vital tissues is another problem encountered only in vivo and must be controlled by some accessory therapy.

All these difficulties point to the necessity of careful study of the circulatory system as related to each type of neoplastic disease. In other words, this is an engineering problem of "plumbing," which has to be adapted for each individual case, supplying enough drug to neoplastic foci while limiting excretion, bypassing liver, and supplying a drug antagonist to other replicating tissues or bypassing them. To achieve maximum labeling conditions with minimum toxicity all these functions should be automatized with proper feedback circuits to monitor and to control the DNA labeling. In other words, the simple operation of adding the drug in the Petri dish or bottle, in the case of tissue culture experiments, becomes a complicated engineering undertaking in the case of a parallel in vivo experiment, with all its fancy control and logistic instrumentation.

This is just one example of the problems that very often have to be faced while applying advances scored by molecular genetics to the clinical field, the area of euphenic engineering. In this field improvements and developments are rather slow, but when successful they are very rewarding from more than one point of view.

A similar and even much more formidable problem would most probably be encountered in trying to translate our in vitro experiments on DNA-mediated genetic transformation of human cell cultures into actual animal experimentation or especially clinical applications. I hope, however, that although the problems will be numerous and the difficulties enormous, we shall not get discouraged too early. A balanced mixture of sound scientific and engineering approaches should overcome in time each new difficulty when it arises. Good luck to euphenics and euphenic engineering!

Dr. Klein

I congratulate the other speakers on the good job they have done, but in order to stimulate discussion, I shall try to challenge them on some views.

First, we have heard the statement that a man in effect becomes a microbe when his somatic cells are isolated and cultivated in vitro. I maintain that a contradiction is implicit in this statement. When we handle somatic cells like microorganisms, we select for unlimited growth of the sort characteristic of microorganisms or cancer cells. In the absence of nutritional and toxicity limitations for growth, they would grow in an unlimited fashion and would convert the whole globe into their own kind in a very short time. When a human cell behaves in that way like a microbe, it is no longer a human cell, much less a man. Higher cells have growth limitations from a superimposed organization. To remain representative of the organism from which they have been derived, they should keep the properties of higher cells. This means that they should remain responsive to growth controls as normal cells are in the organism. You cannot have a cell remain what it is and also do what is not part of the normal behavior of that cell and is in some respects the opposite of normal behavior, at least when it goes on for a prolonged period of time. My contention is that this is asking the impossible.

Moreover, for cells in culture to be representative of man, they should keep their differentiations of structure and function. However, when the cells are free from growth control and put into culture, they lose their ability to differentiate, as has been stated in several chapters, and later die out or else become established cell lines, by which one means that they really grow well and for prolonged periods of time. Far from being normal, representative human cells, all established cell lines that have been adequately studied are said to be neoplastic and highly aneuploid, i.e., they possess unbalanced, abnormal sets of chromosomes. Aneuploidy may or may not be related to the neoplastic transformation, but it is there. There is no evidence at all to show that modern tissue culture can permit the study of cells representative of the normal cell in a higher organism. What one studies, unless fresh explants that are usually considered very impure are used, are in fact cancer cells, whether one realizes it or not. The correctly modified statement then is that one often, if not always, studies cancer when somatic cells are isolated and cultivated in vitro. This may be interesting enough as a model but it should not be confused with the study of normal and representative somatic cells. That is not now possible except in some very special cases.

To make it possible, we have a long way to go. First, we have to revise our whole approach to tissue culture. We have to find media that maintain normal cells even if this means that they cannot be handled as microorganisms. We have to apply an entirely new dimension of techniques to fit a new material. The techniques brought from microbial genetics are wonderful and excellent as models, but they can become a Procrustean bed if we believe that by forcing the cells into them we still have them as we want them to be. A new biological level of organization, the higher cell, creates a new dimension of problems for which the techniques useful at the lower level are not applicable or are insufficient. Dr. Sonneborn has pointed out elsewhere that this will happen at each new level of organization.

Of course it is very easy to make critical remarks and it is very difficult to prove something positive, but the dimensional design that is needed is perhaps growing the cells under conditions of growth control. One example that may be mentioned is that when bone marrow cells are put into culture, they quickly lose their ability to differentiate into blood cells and so cannot save lethally irradiated animals by transplantation and repopulation. On the other hand, if the same cells are put into diffusion chambers within the animal, they grow very much like a tissue culture but keep for long periods of time the ability to differentiate. There is something different here, something lacking in the culture outside the animal and present in the environment provided by the body. If it is present in vivo, why should we not be able to supply it in vitro in either organ culture or other forms of culture? It is certainly not in the type of culture we are using now outside the body with its tremendous selection for rapid growth and dedifferentiation. So the conclusion of this point is that the analogies with microorganisms are based on analogous thinking, not analogous facts, and the hope of easy success may end in disappointment.

A second point: even if it were possible to study normal somatic cells as they are representative of their position in the body, this does not imply that they are representative of the organism as a whole. I challenge the statement that each diploid human cell is the equivalent of an intact human for genetic analysis. This is based on what Dr. Pontecorvo has called a matter of faith: that all somatic cells contain the same genetic information. In support of this faith, we depend essentially on the nature of the mitotic process that we see in a very crude way in the microscope. We have no proof whatever for genetic equality among somatic cells. It is important to stress that very sensible models of genetic differences among somatic cells have been constructed by the maize workers, McClintock and Brink. And while I would in no way imply that the existence of genetic differences among somatic cells has been proved, neither has it been disproved. The differentiations among somatic cells are currently assumed to be due, not to the presence of different genes, but to the repression of different genes in different somatic cells. Some genes function in one kind of somatic cell, other genes of the same set function in another kind of somatic cell. However, in contrast with the reversibility of all known examples of genic repression and derepression in microorganisms, these differentiations are irreversible. Nobody has so far shown that a cell can change from a differentiated stage into a dedifferentiated one and then redifferentiate in another direction, which is exactly what would be required in order to show that the genes are there but only repressed. Maybe they are not there at all. The situation should not be prejudiced by taking anything for granted. The problem is how to find out. As indicated by Dr. Pontecorvo, one may apply biochemical or genetic analysis.

As far as genetic analysis goes, although the first step, cell fusion, has been shown to occur, much more needs to be known about it. So far it has only been found for some very special cell types and no one yet knows whether it is of general occurrence. Further, the second step, segregation of chromosomes, has not been shown to occur in an orderly fashion, although occasionally some chromosomes may be lost. Actually, many experiments weigh against the normal occurrence of an orderly process of fusion and segregation in somatic cells. I will cite one often repeated kind of relevant experiment.

One grows together in mixtures for long periods of time two different kinds of tumor cells each carrying two different allelic genes, a and b, or c and d, respectively, for antigenic markers controlled by the same genic locus. After they have grown together in mixture, they can be put into appropriately selective hosts, for example the original hosts. This cleans up the mixed populations very well, one host eliminating the ab cells, the other the cd cells. You can also look for the four possible new recombinant types, ac, ad, bc, bd, by choosing appropriate new hosts for the tumor cells. But they are never found. Yet they should be if fusion and segregation occurred. Perhaps they do not occur with cells in vivo. However, some very suggestive but not decisive evidence indicates the occurrence in mammalian cells of somatic segregation independently of cell fusion.

Finally, I may mention a few findings regarding mutability. Dr. DeMars pointed out that it is apparently easier to obtain mutations in some cells than in others. We have evidence that there is a great difference in the probability with which a given antigenic mutation will arise in cells of different tumors, although the whole series of tumors (most of them diploid) was induced by the same agents in mice of the same genotype and sometimes in the same mouse. Where and what are the basis of this mutational difference? It could be at the genetic level in the normal cells from which the tumors have originated, but that would imply genetic differences among somatic cells. It could be at the nongenetic level in the normal cells from which the tumors have originated, but that would mean that nongenetic differentiation of somatic cells has an influence on the genetic process of mutation. Finally, it could be at the level of, and inherent to, the neoplastic transformation itself and so would bear on the question of the genetic or nongenetic nature of the neoplastic transformation.

I think all this illustrates the difficulties of analysis, how far we really are from any analytical approach, the nature of the basic tasks ahead, and the long way we have yet to go.

Dr. Pontecorvo

Dr. Klein is quite right in stressing that we do not make man into a microorganism by culturing differentiated somatic cells. But there is some misconception here about the possible uses of human cell cultures for genetic analysis. First, somatic cell cultures can be used as systems for the study of genetic processes in general, regardless of the relations between cultured cells and cells in the intact body. In this case it is perfectly all right to say that we are making man into a microorganism. Unfortunately cell cultures are much less suitable for studying general genetic processes than bacteria. Therefore I do not think there is any point at all in this kind of approach, except as a tool for learning tricks and developing techniques for the second purpose, presently to be mentioned.

Second, there is the sort of use I have mentioned: i.e., short-term cultures of somatic cells as a means for analyzing the genetic constitution of the individual from whom the cells derive. Such cultures from genetically different individual donors can be examined to find: first, which genetically determined differences between individuals are recognizable at the cellular level in cell cultures, and, second, in the cases of differences, recognizable and persistent in cell cultures, how we can use these differences for constructing chromosome maps by means of one or another process of somatic segregation. This does not involve expecting the cell culture to behave as in the whole human being. One only asks which genetically determined differences can at present be identified in body fluids, fresh tissues, cultured cells, and so on. These differences can then be used as genetic markers. That is all there is to it.

Furthermore, one can begin to ask questions about very elementary systems of regulatory processes occurring in these cultured cells, using for instance the approach that I mentioned with 6PGD. This enzyme is known to be produced in certain types of cells in the body, but perhaps not in all. One can then try to find out how to make the latter types of cells develop that particular enzyme. This would be an approach to the processes of induction and repression of the synthesis of particular enzymes.

There is nothing more pretentious, nothing grander than this, in my story at all. If we could, by methods of the kind described, make within a few years human chromosome maps of say 500 genes out of the 50,000 to a million that may exist, it would be a worthwhile operation.

Dr. DeMars. Dr. Klein, you said in effect that man becomes not a microbe in culture but a cancer. The basis for this assertion, if I understand you, is that when we cultivate cells we select for rapid growth. However, rapid growth is not the only criterion of a cancer. All cells in culture grow rapidly at first. Cancer cells grow rapidly in the intact human being. There are only a limited number of cases where cells that have been cultivated have been examined for rapid growth when implanted back in the intact organism. By that criterion of cancerousness, would it not be hard to support your assertion that the cells that we grow in culture are *ipso facto* cancerous?

Dr. Klein. Thank you very much, Drs. Pontecorvo and DeMars. From your comments I think I have certainly stimulated the discussion, which was the purpose of my comments. First, to respond to Dr. Pontecorvo, I am in perfect agreement with him as long as he limits the objectives of cell culture work in the way he did.

But I do not agree with Dr. DeMars because cancer is not just a problem of growth. It is a problem that has to do with cell relationships, with responsiveness to control forces in the organism. Once cells are put into culture and kept there, even if they stay diploid for some time, it is an empirical fact that either they become weaker and weaker and eventually die out, or, by some unknown process, they suddenly become both rapidly growing and capable of indefinite growth. Here emphasis is not on the rate of growth but on its lack of limitation. All such established cell lines that have been reimplanted in a genetically or immunologically compatible body gave rise to tumors that killed or at least grew progressively. So they did not respond to whatever growth controls were present in these organisms. This is the essential thing about cancer, not rapid growth per se. I would be interested if anyone knows of an established cell line that has been in culture for a year or so and that is still certainly normal and not cancerous.

Dr. Luria. In relation to the comments of Drs. Pontecorvo and Klein, I wonder whether we may not be directing attention away from one rather useful purpose of work on human cells and tissue cultures. I am sure all the speakers are quite aware that the most important thing may be the possibility of discovering, through the use of these cell systems, types of mechanisms that we do not yet know and that, once discovered, may bring new powers of intervention. Such discoveries can only be made, or at least are most likely to be made, by studying the simplified cell culture systems. For example, I think Dr. Pontecorvo would be the last one to believe that the systems of regulation that are beginning to be understood in bacteria are going to apply to, or are going to be the only ones that occur in, mammalian cells. I, at least, think that other levels of regulation will be discovered.

Let us take a typical example of what one can expect at a given time and what later actually happens. Until 1960 everybody was convinced that the coding problem, the problem of the way the alphabet of the RNA is translated into that of polypeptide, would have to be solved through the hard, painful work of analyzing the fine structure of a gene and the fine structure of the polypeptide produced by that gene and then matching them one by one. But what actually happened? How was the problem solved? By two totally unanticipated brilliant insights and new discoveries. First, Crick saw that mutations of a certain type could be used for studying the number of nucleotides involved in a code word. Second, Nirenberg realized, from an unexpected experimental result the possibility of coding in vitro by means of artificially constructed polynucleotides.

So the important thing is to have a system such as the cell in culture that can be manipulated on many more dimensions than the isolated organs or the intact mammal. In this sense, I think that cell cultures are not cancer or microorganisms but the most hopeful materials one can have for discovering genetic processes of a new type.

Question from audience. Have there been any efforts at trying to discover conditions that would direct cells in culture to undergo meiosis or comparable processes, where the stages of synapsis and so on might be used to analyze translocations, inversions, and other chromosomal aberrations?

Dr. Pontecorvo: Not that I know.

Dr. Muller. When I was in the Soviet Union I came across one experiment by a Dr. Zhivago (not the fictitious one) in which he was cultivating (in 1935) human leukocytes and found that in certain types of hypertonic solutions the chromosomes paired up two by two, somewhat as they do at meiosis. He died soon afterwards, and as far as I know, that was never followed up. But that at least is a possibly hopeful lead in that direction.

Question from audience. Can one distinguish the cell cultures that will induce cancer on reimplantation in the host from cell cultures that grow normally after reinsertion?

Dr. DeMars. First, in the case of the infection of hamster cells with polyoma virus, a virus that leads to the production of cancer, infection of the cells is accompanied by production of a new antigen. Whether or not this has something to do with the malignancy is not known. Nevertheless, in this case, the altered antigenic makeup of the cells distinguishes them from normal cells and is a reliable indicator of their malignant nature, even after the virus itself is no longer detectable.

The question asked also comes back to something that Dr. Klein said. He said that cells that somehow have learned to grow indefinitely long in culture are always malignant cells with abnormal chromosomes. According to my reading, no matter how long they have been in culture, cells derived from normal tissues do not grow persistently or invasively. On the other hand, cells derived from malignant tissues do grow. This is the work of Dr. George Foley, in Boston, who has tested many, many different strains of cells.

Dr. Klein. Dr. Foley found that both grow. The normal ones grow with a large inoculum, but both grow.

Dr. DeMars. Yes, that is right. There is a very large quantitative difference. You might need a thousand times more cells of normal origin than cells of malignant origin to obtain growth in the body.

Dr. Zamenhof (of Columbia University, College of Physicians and Surgeons). I would like to call attention to certain developments that may influence the evolution of man only because they may improve our main tool, our brain, which made possible all that has been discussed here and will make possible all the things in the future. The nerve cells in our brain, or the cortical neurons, cease dividing in about the fourth or fifth month of fetal or embryonic life in man, and shortly after birth in the rat. Some time ago we reported (*Physiol. Zool.,* **15:** 281, 1942) that if the rats are treated with the anterior pituitary growth hormone that stimulates cell division before the normal time for the cells to cease dividing, they have larger brains and 86 per cent more neurons when born. This superiority partly persisted until maturity. When the rats were tested for intelligence in a maze, they were found to be somewhat more intelligent. Recently in England Clendinnen and Eayrs (*Endocrinology,* **22:** 183, 1961) repeated and confirmed these results. Thus it appears that early administration of growth hormone may increase the number of our neurons and improve our intelligence.

PART III

Evaluation of Applications to Man

CHAPTER 5

Means and Aims in Human Genetic Betterment

Herman J. Muller, Zoology Department
Indiana University

The main thesis I wish to uphold in this paper is the following. For any group of people who have a rational attitude toward matters of reproduction, and who also have a genuine sense of their own responsibility to the next and subsequent generations, the means exist right now of achieving a much greater, speedier, and more significant genetic improvement of the population, by the use of selection, than could be effected by the most sophisticated methods of treatment of the genetic material that might be available in the twenty-first century. The obstacles to carrying out such an improvement by selection are psychological ones, based on antiquated traditions from which we can emancipate ourselves, but the obstacles to doing so by treatment of the genetic material are substantive ones, rooted in the inherent difficulties of the physicochemical situation.

To be sure, these physicochemical difficulties present us with stimulating challenges that warrant extraordinary efforts on our part. They are difficulties that can increasingly be overcome, and the assault against them is bound to yield most rewarding and often unexpected benefits all along the way. However, it would be intellectually dishonest and morally reprehensible of us to exploit the hope of mankind's eventual success in this enterprise as an excuse for not giving our support to the great re-educational process that could make possible, by means now physically available, a most significant advance in the genetic constitution of our species.

Actually, there is no rational basis for regarding the two methods—which I will here refer to as genetic surgery and parental selection, respectively—as being alternative or in any degree mutually antagonistic. In fact, they should eventually reinforce one another in a more or less complementary fashion. But in the long meantime, before the surpassing refinements of the hoped-for genetic surgery become available, it would be a subterfuge unworthy of scientific thinking to hide from the genuine potentialities of the present behind the screen of the indefinite future. Moreover, persons pursuing this policy would thereby be relinquishing to others the influence they might otherwise exert on the way in which parental selection will be practiced. For, like other techniques capable of either helping or harming man, it is bound to come into eventual use anyway, notwithstanding social impediments. And, as I will later try to show, this is likely to happen long before genetic surgery becomes widely feasible. It is better, then, to have the way paved as well as possible for a salutary kind of parental selection rather than for a pernicious kind.

Techniques of Genetic Surgery

But before going into the matter of parental selection let us try to gain some idea of the possibilities of genetic surgery. So torrential and unexpected has been the flood of progress of the last ten years in physicochemical genetics, that is, in our understanding of the mechanisms that form the basis of all terrestrial life, that it is no wonder that some persons, especially those less familiar with life's elaborations, have been swept off their feet, and have come to think that they have almost arrived at a millennium of biological omniscience and omnipotence. Similarly, some physical scientists of the seventeenth century, dazzled by their new insights, dreamed that all knowledge lay only just beyond their contemporary horizon. As compared with those past advances, however, today's progress in basic genetics is inordinately greater, not only in rate, but also in depth and volume, and it surely ranks among the most magnificent and thrilling of all scientific revolutions that mankind has achieved thus far. Those who would belittle it are only succeeding in belittling themselves. And yet, it would be equally a mistake to minimize the magnitude of the tasks still ahead.

Authors of earlier chapters in this book have called attention to some of the difficulties that would have to be overcome in order to effect a desired, prespecified change in the genetic constitution of a human cell. As they have pointed out, and as Dr. Sonneborn (1) had maintained still earlier, two general methods are at present conceivable for this purpose, although neither is yet in sight of general application. The more remote of these methods would involve altering in a definite way a given unit in a chromosome, that is, causing a *directed mutation* of a given nucleotide in a DNA thread. This would be done, it is proposed, by first obtaining or synthesizing, and then introducing into one or more cells, a chain of units which in general was homologous or complementary to the portion of DNA to be "operated on." This introduced piece, it is hoped, could under appropriate circumstances become conjugated in parallel position with the portion of chromosome to be changed. Previously the introduced piece would have had to be so treated as to carry at the strategic point in it, corresponding to the unit in the original chromosome that required alteration, a chemical group of appropriate reactivity that we may call a mutagen. This mutagen, then, would be expected to cause the desired type of change at the right point in the original chromosome.

In the other method, which might be termed that of *partial crossing*, an already improved portion of a chromosome would be substituted for the inferior portion originally present in the cell. As before, the procedure would require one first to get a corresponding piece of chromosome (synthetic or natural) from elsewhere. The introduced piece would in this case have to be identical with the piece native to the cell except that, at the strategic point in it, corresponding to the unit that is to be improved, it already possessed a unit (a nucleotide or group of nucleotides) of the desired type. Hopefully, influences would then be brought to bear that would cause the introduced, superior piece to conjugate in parallel with the original chromosome, and then to undergo the type of exchange with it known as crossing over. Thereby the introduced piece, or at least a part of it, containing the desired type of unit, would become incorporated in the cell's genetic material, while the unwanted original portion would be cast out or destroyed.

It must be admitted that in both these schemes considerable flights of fancy are involved, at which many safe and sane scientists may laugh. Nevertheless, their laughs would in due time be drowned in the water that keeps flowing under the bridge.

At present, though, there are only bare beginnings, applicable in a few rare instances in microorganisms, of procedures for physically isolating or treating given portions of the genetic material. Moreover, methods have not yet been developed by which it would be practicable to determine the precise sequence of the thousands of units, that is, of nucleotides, that characterizes any given gene of a higher organism. Nor have we methods now for constructing such a long exact sequence artificially even if we knew its arrangements, nor for incorporating some chemical mutagen in it or in the natural structure at just one or more desired points. Finally, we do not yet know how to induce an introduced piece of chromosome (or of chromosome homologue or analogue) to become conjugated in parallel to the corresponding piece of a native chromosome, in the cell of a higher organism, and then to undergo appropriate exchange, that is, crossing over, with that native chromosome. In cells of vertebrates, in fact, even the two complete homologous chromosomes of a pair, one descended from the mother and the other from the father, although both present naturally in the same cell of the body, have not been known to conjugate and undergo exchange at all except under the special, unknown conditions that normally exist within germ cells as they are preparing to mature, although there are a few cases in which such occurrences among somatic cells have been suspected.

It is true that in the brilliant pioneer work of Szybalski and Szybalska at Wisconsin with mammalian cells in culture, this process of "partial crossing" may have been induced in them in a non-directed way—sometimes for one chromosome portion and sometimes for another. Moreover, granting this, it could be ascertained, for one particular pair of genes having a well-recognized effect, when some such exchange had taken place. However, accepting the occurrence of some kind of "partial crossing" here, the possibility is by no means excluded that what happened was a relatively gross event: namely, that an entire chromosome rather than a part of a chromosome had entered a cell and had become established in it intact. The achievement would nevertheless have been a great one even in that case, for as yet no one has even succeeded in transferring a whole chromosome in living material by the more obvious method of micromanipulation. Moreover, that method would be still more strictly limited to whole chromosomes, since they could hardly be visually identified and handled except when in condensed form.

Even if it became practicable to carry out transfers of some such kind between cells, with respect to some particular genetic component, it would not yet be possible to control the heredity of a future individual in the given particular, unless one of the cells thus altered, or at least its nucleus, could later be cultivated or manipulated in such a way as to take part in the formation of mature germ cells, or else, more directly, in the constitution of a fertilized egg. I know of only one piece of work undertaken in the last quarter of a century—that reported by Kodani (2) in a short but striking abstract—in which the attempt was made to cultivate vertebrate germ cells outside the body, and to find the conditions under which they could be induced to mature, obvious though the need has been for such work. Moreover, there have, so far as I know, been no reports whatever of attempts—whether successful or not—to transfer the nuclei of cells in culture to unfertilized or fertilized eggs that were then placed under conditions conducive to their development into an individual. It seems strange that despite all the discussion about learning to control the genetic constitution so few people appear to be concerned with such objectives. The attainment of them would seem to be so much simpler than the solution of the highly recondite problems that we have previously discussed. But a mastery of these nearer ends would be equally essential for successful application of genetic surgery, and it would also be of both practical and theoretical importance even without that ultimate refinement of techniques.

Diagnosing for Genetic Surgery

Let us suppose, however, that the technical difficulties of performing genetic surgery for *any* prespecified portion of any chromosome, or—at worst—for the whole of any prespecified chromosome, have at last been overcome, and that such microsurgery or, rather, nanosurgery ("nano" designating a scale a thousand times smaller than "micro") is a really practicable mode of procedure. Suppose, further, that the cell nucleus resulting from such an operation can be made to serve for the development of an individual. To what extent will all this enable us to control the human genetic constitution in desired ways?

It is obvious that it can do so only when one or both of two conditions are met—depending on whether we are to use directed mutation or partial crossing. For directed mutation, we must be able to find out exactly what chromosome, or chromosome region, or nucleotide, should be changed, and to what form it should be changed, in order to achieve the particular final effect wanted. For partial crossing, we must know what site is to be changed and must be able to supply, as substitute genetic material, a chromosome or chromosome region that already incorporates the given improvement. In either case, then, the trait in question must have been tracked down at least to its chromosome in the cell to be treated and, if there is a donor cell, in that cell also. But as yet, in man, except for the fact that some traits are known to have their genes in the X chromosome, there are only feeble beginnings of such knowledge.

Nor is this knowledge easily acquired by means presently in use, for many people have long been working to increase it. But there may always, of course, be some new methodological breakthrough. Such, for example, would be provided if some automatic wholesale screening procedure were devised that utilized complementation or conjugation, a procedure based in part on the methods of Spiegelman (3) and his group, which are somewhat analogous to those used in some immunological studies. Conceivably, such a procedure might pin-point, bind, or extract any chromosome region that all individuals of one group, which contained a given trait, agreed in being alike in, and that all individuals of another group, not containing that trait, differed from the first group in regard to. As of now, no such procedure is in sight.

It should be realized that such a method could work only if the individuals screened had first been correctly classified with respect to the given trait and if the trait, as classified, was dependent on just one specific chromosome region. The method would break down in multiple-factor cases, that is, in those in which the given phenotypic category could be the expression of different genes, occupying diverse positions. Moreover, except for a relatively small group of traits that are dependent on individual proteins, most hereditary characteristics are in fact of this multiple-factor nature and therefore not amenable to such a method. Most of these same traits vary quantitatively, being of different grades, depending on just what combination of the genes for them happens to be present.

This stricture applies more especially to the traits of greatest importance for humanity, such as the general level of intelligence, the native strength of social predispositions, general vigor, and longevity. Moreover, the same difficulty even applies to most of the components of any of these complex traits. That is, the components into which they could be factored by the presently existing methods of medicine or psychology are themselves the product of many genes. It is of course to be expected that some day more searching methods of analysis will be devised, and that eventually these may even go so far as to reach underlying differences, represented, let us say, by specific proteins, which in turn depended directly on individual genes. Even today a few rare abnormalities are known whose genes, though unlocated, have been found to result in highly distinctive biochemical differences. Excluding such special cases, however, analysis at the protein or gene level is not yet in sight for the major quantitatively varying characters.

Yet even if the possibility of complete analysis of this kind were actually at hand, the results would be bewilderingly complex. In fact, for a very long time to come, the more of these details we knew, the more we would feel baffled in trying to attain some scientific control over the genetic composition of the germ cells of the ordinary individual, by means of the punctiform type of intervention that advanced techniques of genetic surgery might conceivably afford.

This seeming paradox results from the staggering complexity of the genetic basis of any highly elaborated ability of the organism. It also results from the complexity, compounded upon this, of the web of gene-dependent and simultaneously environment-dependent biochemical processes that constitute the development of these abilities in the immature stages of the individual, and their maintenance, functioning, and readjustment throughout his life. With the exception of relatively rare specific cases, we will not be able to alter human genetic material understandingly, in the knowledge of how our alterations really work, in a manner comparable to that in which a mechanic might knowingly repair or improve an automobile, until we can follow through the details of these overwhelming complexities of both the genetic material and its organized web of products.

To appreciate this difficulty more realistically, let us recall that one set of human genes contains some 4 billion pairs of nucleotides, of four types, in precise linear arrangement, and that there are reasons to infer that relatively few of these are nonfunctional or superfluous. Thus the substitution of a nucleotide of one type by one of another type—which is probably the usual kind of mutation—is likely to affect to some extent one or more characteristics of the organism developing from a set of genes thus changed. The change would in the great majority of cases be detrimental. Moreover, it would be likely to affect the degree and type of development of one or more of the general abilities or propensities we have designated above as the most important ones.

Now, in the present world population of about 3 billion people (comprising 6 billion complete sets of genes) there must exist, scattered about, practically every one of the physically possible types of nucleotide substitutions, or "point mutations." Since three different substitutions are possible for each nucleotide this makes a total of some 3 times 4 billion, that is, 12 billion different genetic changes. Lacking here would be only the relatively few that act as strongly dominant lethals or steriles. From our rough knowledge of mutation frequencies and degree of dominance we can calculate that any one of the surviving nearly 12 billion types of mutant structure would usually exist in a number of different individuals. Moreover, not a few of them would exist in many individuals. (We are assuming here, for simplicity, that at least 4 billion others can be classed as "normal," and we are purposely evading a discussion of the range that "normality" may have.) Thus each person must carry his own characteristic "load of mutations," comprising a combination different from that of any other person unless he has an identical twin.

How long will it be before we can have a type of analysis by which it will be practicable to work out the entire sequence of 4 billion units of both sets of genes (one derived from the father and one from the mother) of every one of our 3 billion people? How long will it be, after that, before we can know just which nucleotide sites or even which whole genes and combinations of genes, in any given case, would cause given shortcomings in an important trait if, as usual, that trait had a highly multiple-factor basis, capable of enormous variation from one individual to another? Before such a diagnosis could be made it would not be possible to rectify the defect, even if our genetic surgery was so refined that we could alter any nucleotide at will, or if our partial-crossing methods allowed us to implant any chosen whole chromosome, or any chosen chromosome region, from a cell of one line of descent into that of another. True, scanning methods might some time be developed to aid in the recognition of given traits in cell cultures. But this would still leave us far from the knowledge that, in a multiple-factor system of ten thousand varying genes, could predict just what combination would result in the desired development of the finished character of the adult individual.

Even after we were able to ascertain which nucleotides or which genes in a given case were the cause of a given abnormality (or supernormality), and after we had learned to change or substitute such parts at will, we would still and for a long time to come be working, in the main, in a highly empirical fashion, far removed from the method of the mechanic and still further from that of the engineer, for we would still have only a generalized knowledge of how the genes actually work in the construction and functioning of the organism. Despite the triumphs of molecular genetics and of biochemical physiology in disclosing mechanisms of synthesis, of construction and reconstruction of cell substances and cell structures, of energy transfer and enzymatic cycles, of gene repression and instigation, and soon, perhaps, of processes of embryogeny and differentiation, nevertheless these are only the great girders of life's organization. They are supported, modified, guided in innumerable subtle ways by interacting gene products, products of products, and, further, products *n* times removed from the genes themselves.

Even such essential proteins as hemoglobin and the major enzymes each have a multitude of units, amino acids precisely tied together, and for most of these amino acids there is a functional value in having it where it is, otherwise the arrangement could not have been so persistent as to have remained alike even in different genera and families. When we say we have found that only a part of the molecule is necessary for its characteristic action, that merely means that we are still ignorant of the roles of the other parts, which under certain circumstances must be significant. But if the complication of these substances more directly produced by the genes is so great, how much greater must be the subsequent complications, which are represented by the vast web of interactions taking place in multiple-factor determinations of the traits or abilities that we are ordinarily concerned with? If merely reading off the succession of the 4 billion nucleotides that lay the basis for a man is such a monstrous task, how incredibly titanic must be the job of finding out just how all these parts, through devious successions of intricately interwoven processes, finally make the man as we find him? Despite future aid from automated tools and calculators, here is work for many lifetimes, on the part of successive hosts of investigators. And if the job ever approached what might be termed completion, no one person or small group of persons, built as people are today, could have an adequate grasp of more than a relatively small portion of the whole. We are far too complicated for our individual selves to understand—even those of us who are physicists!

Thus even a very precise genetic surgery, guided by a highly elaborate diagnosis of genetic constitutions, would still have to be largely empirical. It would be empirical in that, in the main, it would undertake given operations because its evidence indicated that these operations would lead to the desired final results, but knowledge of how these final results followed from the operations performed would still be lacking, for the most part. This being the case, moreover, mistakes would sometimes be made, for in the absence of precise knowledge of the nature of the processes involved, a given operation might be carried out that gave an unexpected outcome because of the presence of some other, interacting gene or environmental condition, the potentialities of which in that particular combination had not previously been tested out. This is not to say that the genetic surgery would not be worth doing anyway but, despite its exactness in technique, it would still remain for the most part empirical in its attainment of its aims. Moreover, in addition to the particular genes on which attention was being focused, there would in any given case be several or many other genes, subject to a random type of distribution that would introduce highly unpredictable features into the result obtained.

No doubt the human organism is far more complicated than it would have to be for the attainment of the powers and faculties that it is endowed with. But its complications, having once arisen through the indirect, patchwork way in which evolution has taken place, are now built-in needs. We have to maintain them and to repair their damages, and we might improve them by further patching. Once we have mastered the essentials of the whole picture, however, and seen through the nonessentials, the time might even come when we yearned to follow old Omar's wish, that is, "to seize this sorry scheme of things entire, and mold it nearer to the heart's desire." Then, by rebuilding from the ground up, we might, if we were clever enough, do much better than nature has done.

Following this idea, some thoughtful persons (e.g., Arthur C. Clarke [4]) are even taking the position, quite seriously, that we may after a while succeed in creating a type of robot that is much more efficient and intelligent and even socially, ethically, and esthetically better oriented than a man is. Perhaps he could be made, "from whole cloth" as it were (or from whole metal!), much more easily than man could be radically remade. At any rate, he would doubtless be much simpler in design than a man, and he would be correspondingly easier to understand, repair, and improve upon. Furthermore, he should be able to do all that for himself. Thus, there may in time be a race between genetic surgery and robotics, and we may find that "this old house will do no longer." Not that I hold a creative genetic surgery to be utterly visionary, in the long view, but I do not hold robotics to be utterly visionary either.

However that may be, the earlier stages of genetic surgery, if it does come into use, will doubtless be concerned mainly with repairing germ cells having certain rare and extreme genetic defects, such as the idiocy caused by failure in handling the amino acid phenylalanine. In this negative role of the technique there will be no more question of values than there is for a surgeon of the more usual kind, for everyone would agree that such marked defects are undesirable. There is nevertheless a problem of values or ethics in deciding for which people it is justifiable to make an effort if, as seems likely, the effort were too great to be applicable to every such case. But in making these decisions we would be thrown back on the whole ethical question of who should reproduce, and to what extent. And until genetic surgery acquires such finesse as readily to make a sage out of a simpleton, a saint out of a scamp, and a Samson out of a shrimp, we will continue to have this problem with us.

Conceivably, we might some day achieve such seeming miracles of genetic metamorphosis as these, by manipulating certain specific genetic sites or chromosomes and thus providing genes that exerted major influences on the general abilities in question. It would at the same time be desirable, in such cases, to obtain as high concentrations as possible of the very numerous correlative or modifying genes that act, sometimes very subtly, to support the major ones, as by regulating and giving balance to their expression. However, it would be a task of transcendent magnitude, intricacy, and reconditeness to do all this by genetic surgery for any one individual. Moreover, every individual to be operated on would present his own unique complex of labyrinthine problems of this sort.

If at length, however, the techniques were mastered that did enable genetic surgeons to tackle in a really practicable way the stupendous tasks of producing to order genetically improved types of human beings, then they would find themselves face to face with the age-old problem of what human values they should strive for—a problem here couched in genetic terms. This problem, even in its genetic form, is not unique for genetic surgery, however. It applies equally to any conceivable scheme for genetic betterment, and it has been used by critics as an argument against any such attempt.

Types of Parental Selection

For persons who would concede the desirability of human genetic betterment, or at least the need of merely preventing genetic deterioration, the possibility of conducting it by some kind of parental selection should not be overlooked, for the technical difficulties of such an approach are incomparably less than those of genetic surgery, in view of the enormous wealth of diverse genetic combinations that are already in existence in any human population. Moreover, the potentialities of these combinations can be assessed in a rough and ready way by methods similar to those obtaining under natural selection, namely, by using the criterion of the given individual's performance. It seems truly perverse for people to wait until they can take the long way around and manufacture genetic constitutions to order, when they are, in large measure, already available. Let us then consider in what ways the genetics of existing populations might be influenced through parental selection, so as to decrease the frequency of genetic defects and to increase the abundance of traits that are considered desirable.

We may first dismiss as obviously biased and pernicious the claims of racists who see in their own race a markedly superior type of humanity or who, conversely, single out certain other races for special condemnation. We may likewise give short shrift to those old-style eugenists who, regarding economic, social, or educational status as a reliable enough criterion of genetic fitness, have advocated measures that would make it easier for the so-called upper classes to have children and harder for the so-called lower classes.

A recent, rather sophisticated modification of the last-mentioned notion is the proposal that certain types of occupations should be so designed as to be attractive to persons of genetically less desirable types, and that the circumstances of these jobs should be so arranged as to make it relatively inconvenient and unattractive for these workers to have children. On the other hand, conversely, certain other types of occupations should, on this view, be so contrived as to be attractive to persons of more fortunate endowments, and these occupations should be associated with ways of living made conducive to the rearing of large families. It is hard to criticize this proposal seriously unless it is spelled out much more concretely. We should, however, point out that exactly this matter of finding a suitable concrete form for it would be a source of much difficulty, especially since the system of values of genetic traits implied in the given concrete arrangement would have to be one that people could agree on. We should also point out that it is highly unlikely that any democratic society would consent to having such intentional restraints imposed on it.

In general, any type of eugenics in which, as in this proposed case, the standards and values are decided upon by governmental bodies is to be regarded with suspicion, even if the government is of some democratic form, for, as yet at least, governments, including relatively enlightened ones, represent in some respects the lowest common denominator of progressive thinking. (In fact, a distinguished scientist on reading this remark has commented that it is in his opinion an understatement.) Nevertheless, it can be heartily agreed that enlightened governments, by their support of free public education, freedom of expression, and scientific research, do indirectly fill a highly useful function in human advancement. That is, they can increase people's opportunities for finding roads to progress.

Now among the most important educational needs of modern populations are those in the area of genetics and evolution. The so-called "common man" already has sufficient native intelligence and social consciousness to be able, when suitably taught, to appreciate the importance of both a good heredity and a good environment, to realize that the betterment of both is to be sought for, and to find gratification in contributing efforts of his own for these common purposes of mankind. Moreover, he is so constituted as readily to adopt a value system in which high regard is given to such primary human psychological attributes as those of sympathy, moral courage, reasonableness, and creativity. This being the case, the most fundamental basis is at hand, through education, for preparing people to follow, voluntarily, courses of action that will on the whole be conducive to the genetic betterment of the species.

Among such courses of action the type most commonly thought of consists of the exercise of more restraint in having children on the part of the genetically less well endowed and the raising of larger families by the better endowed. To this recommendation it should be answered, first, that few people of inferior mentality are willing to appraise themselves as below the average in this respect. Second, those of lower-than-average moral fiber can hardly be expected to exercise unusual restraint in the interest of a higher moral fiber for mankind in general. On the other hand, third, persons of higher-than-average mental ability or of unusually conscientious or considerate disposition are often the very ones most likely to limit their families, in order to enable both themselves, their spouses, and the children whom they do have to live a life more rewarding in other respects. Certainly people's estimates of themselves and of those closest to them are notoriously biased and unrealistic.

At best, then, the attempt to inculcate policies of this kind could have but a small positive effect on genetic trends. Perhaps this effect would be hardly enough to counteract fully the trend toward genetic deterioration that must exist today in technically advanced countries, with their low death and birth rates. This trend results partly from the fact that in these countries the easier reproductive course to follow, at least on the critical occasions, is that which leads to having children, while the more difficult course, the one calling for more self-control, foresight, conscientiousness, and skill, is that by which conception is prevented. In this way the course of genetic selection tends to become reversed.

It is true that people's judgment in regard to such matters could be clarified somewhat, and their resolution strengthened, by advice from specialists, such as those of the heredity and marriage clinics that are increasingly being established. However, a good deal of the attention of such clinics is devoted to influencing, not so much the relative frequencies of genes in the population, but their manner of distribution, through choice of marriage partners. What is sought here is, on the one hand, the promotion of the concentration of valuable traits in given lines of descent and, on the other hand, the hindering of that coming together of identical recessive defects from both parents which leads to those defects being more strongly manifested. These efforts, although helpful for the families directly concerned, do not in themselves act to raise the genetic level of the general population or even to prevent its decline.

A salutary genetic effect may, however, be produced when advice to limit or prevent their reproduction is given to people who are found to carry (or to be likely to carry in latent form) certain genes for extreme defects, such as those causing known types of blindness or idiocy. Yet it must be emphasized that in large measure such judgments only reflect our present ignorance, for it is probable that practically every one of us carries, in more or less latent form, more than one actual "lethal equivalent," that is, a gene or gene-group so defective that, in an offspring who receives it from both parents, it will cause death before maturity is reached. Thus, by the same criterion as that used in the special cases of those now warned not to reproduce, the whole population would become exterminated.

It seems likely, therefore, that for the present and a considerable period to come our knowledge of what genetic defects people carry in hidden form will be so fragmentary as to be of little use for the purpose of substantially reducing the frequency of severe genetic defects—the main objective of negative eugenics today. Of far greater consequence for the population, however, than the avoidance of the sporadic outcroppings of such hidden defects would be the raising of the general genetic level in regard to the abilities and proclivities of greatest human importance. In order to achieve major practical results along these lines it would not be necessary, nor would it for a long time be possible, to arrive at an exact knowledge of the genes and gene-differences involved. They are undoubtedly very numerous, but they give evidence of having, on the whole, a fair amount of dominance. Thus—except for the confusing influence of cultural and other environmental differences—a kind of over-all estimate of an individual's genetic level in regard to these attributes, one having considerable validity, could be obtained by considerations of his actual performance or, as the geneticist would say, his phenotypic classification (not meaning merely his looks!). This is in fact how nature operates in the process of natural selection and how man has operated in past times in the artificial selection of other animals and of plants, and the method has obviously worked. In such over-all appraisals, moreover, one or more highly valuable traits often more than make up for considerable shortcomings.

A heredity clinic would hardly dare to offer advice along these lines to people in general, and if it did, the advice would probably be discounted and resented. Many people would hold, and often quite rightly, that the fact of the advisor's being a geneticist or a physician does not necessarily make him a good judge of what constitute the higher human values, or of the degree to which they, the judged, measure up to reasonable standards in these respects. Yet, as we have noted previously, their own judgments of themselves would also tend to be biased, as they might well admit themselves during moods of unusual calm and objectivity. Does this situation force us to conclude, then, that all doors to parental selection of a salutary and significant kind are closed for the human species?

There has for some time been still another possible method of parental selection, which in large measure avoids these difficulties. This is a method I discussed in a public lecture given at the University of Chicago in 1925, and in a book (5) published in 1935, and that I have recently called germinal choice (6). It is a method that Herbert Brewer (7) independently thought of and wrote on in 1935 and 1939 and termed eutelegenesis, and that Julian Huxley (8), who is favorably disposed toward it, has sometimes referred to as preadoption. Recently Aldous Huxley (9), in his novel *Island,* has also approved of the method, as therein depicted. Something of the same sort was also advocated, independently, by the well-known Russian geneticist A. S. Serebrowsky (10), in 1929.

Unlike what is true of other forms of parental selection that have been suggested for man, this method does not work by attempting to influence either the size of families that people have or their choice of marriage partners. Neither does it attempt to influence people's evaluations of themselves. Its proposed mode of procedure is to establish banks of stored germ cells (spermatozoa), eventually ample banks, derived from persons of very diverse types but including as far as possible those whose lives had given evidence of outstanding gifts of mind, merits of disposition and character, or physical fitness. From these germinal stores couples would have the privilege of selecting such material, for the engendering of children of their own families, as appeared to them to afford the greatest promise of endowing their children with the kind of hereditary constitution that came nearest to their own ideals.

As an aid in making these choices there would be provided as full documentation as possible concerning the donors of the germinal material, the lives they had led, and their relatives. The couples concerned would also have advice available from geneticists, physicians, psychologists, experts in the fields of activity of the donors being considered, and other relevant specialists, as well as generalizers. In order to allow a better perspective to be obtained on the donors themselves and on their genetic potentialities, as well as to minimize personality fads and to avoid risks of personal entanglements, it would be preferable for the material used to have been derived from donors who were no longer living, and to have been stored for at least 20 years. The technique of preparing semen in a medium containing glycerine and keeping it at the temperature of liquid nitrogen, as worked out by a succession of investigators, such as Hoagland and Pincus (11, 12), and recently improved for human material by J. K. Sherman (13), provides a reliable and relatively inexpensive means of maintaining such material for an unlimited period without deterioration.

Problems and Opportunities of Germinal Choice

It has been estimated that thousands of children per year are engendered in the United States by artificial insemination of women whose husbands are sterile with sperm derived from donors. The choosing of these donors is always carried out solely by the clinician, and their identity is kept strictly secret even from the couple concerned. It is ironical that, so far as known, the method of controlled insemination has not yet been used for genetic purposes except in occasional cases in which the husband, although fertile, has some specific defect of a hereditary kind, or a blood group incompatible with the wife's. The chief aim of the clinician seems to be to produce a child who can readily be mistaken for a genetic child of the husband's, and then to pretend that nature took its course in the usual way. Thus, in most of these cases, the golden opportunity has been thrown away that might have led to the creation of an especially worthy human being. Moreover, each individual human life is in itself a matter of cardinal significance.

Undoubtedly many of the couples who have resorted to this procedure would have jumped at the chance of having their child derived from germinal material of unusual promise, and some of them would even have had the moral courage not to dissimulate about their enterprise. This would in turn give encouragement to those realistic idealists who, though not burdened by sterility or unusual defect, would actually prefer to have a child who had resulted from the exercise of their own studied choice, rather than risk the still greater uncertainties of favorable outcome that natural procreation would have entailed. My experience in talking with people on this subject has convinced me that we Americans are not such a nation of sheep in this respect and that, if the opportunity of germinal choice were opened, a gradually increasing number of seemingly "normal" couples, in addition to a large proportion of those afflicted with seminal inadequacy or obvious genetic defect, would elect to use this means of having at least a part of their family. Moreover, as the saying goes, "nothing succeeds like success," and the obvious successes achieved by this method would within a generation win it still more adherents. It would constitute a major extension of human freedom in a quite new direction.

Of course, as would be emphasized to everyone volunteering for this mode of reproduction, even the most careful germinal choice will, with our present highly empirical criteria, leave an immense area of uncertainty, that is, a wide range of possibilities for any individual offspring. That is because of the large role played by chance in determining, first, just what genes of either parent any given fertilized egg receives, and, second, what role the environment played in determining the characteristics of the parents and what role it will play in determining those of the child. But despite these considerable uncertainties, a whole group of children produced by careful germinal choice is sure to be significantly influenced, in regard to the traits chiefly chosen for, in the direction of that selection. An individual is rarely outstanding in a particular ability or predisposition unless not only his environment but also his heredity was markedly inclined in that direction. And the genetic constitution of the child stands halfway, on the average, between those of his two parents. Accordingly, the over-all upgrading in such a group of cases would be clear.

At present social taboos, especially as they exist in the mind of the physician, present the chief obstacle to the beginning of the practice of germinal choice. But social taboos have never held up indefinitely when opportunities to benefit by disregarding them were offered by new techniques. Aside from this obstacle, the main psychological impediment to the practice of germinal choice lies in its violation of the principle of genetic proprietorship that so many men hold dear: the feeling that somehow they survive through the genes of their child, especially if he be a son (though in fact the son carries about 5 per cent fewer of the father's genes than the daughter does). There is no instinct directly involved here, since it is necessarily absent in peoples who lack knowledge of the process of procreation. It is in fact a kind of mystique, and ignores the facts of dispersal and recombination of genes in the course of a few generations made clear by a greater knowledge of genetics. It also comes off a poor second in comparison with the justified pride that would be elicited in the social father or, shall we say, the "love father," of a germinally chosen child, through his realization that this child was a product of his deliberate volition, rather than of his reflexes, and that the child embodies the best genetic, as well as the best environmental influences, that he was able to provide it with. Reciprocally, the child would feel gratitude and close kinship with his love father.

With the coming of a better understanding of genetics and evolution the individual's fixation on the attempted perpetuation of just his particular genes will be bound to fade. It will be superseded by a more rational view, supported by just as strong a feeling, according to which the individual finds fulfillment in passing on to the future the best that he can find to represent him, by gathering that best from wherever it can be found in most concentrated form. And he will condemn as a childish conceit the notion that there is any reason for his unessential peculiarities, idiosyncrasies, and foibles to be expressed generation after generation. In these ways, as well as through the love and careful upbringing that he bestows upon his child of choice, he will achieve a form of continuance as worthy of himself as possible, one expressing a higher form of morality than that now prevalent.

It need not be feared that couples actuated by thoughts and feelings of this kind are likely, in the over-all picture, to make bad mistakes in their selection of major aims, or of the genetic material intended to serve those aims. Couples so enlightened as to resort in this or the next generation to germinal choice will not require a corps of axiologists or sociologists to tell them what are the most crying genetic needs of man of today. They will have come to realize that our stone age genetic constitutions are being sorely stretched in trying to adapt to the unprecedented complications of civilization and of the world as seen by modern science, to the need to feel brotherhood for 3 billion people, and to the responsibility of guiding without disaster the use of the enormous powers that scientific technology has created. It will be evident to them that the need is both for better brains in depth and breadth, with all the faculties accessory thereto, and for warmer hearts, which allow men to find more genuine fulfillment in actions that serve humanity at large.

This is a far cry from the long-term planning of some organism superior to man. It represents the action called for by present-day needs, and aims at very nearby goals. Such goals are the ever more abundant production of people who combine the greatest gifts of mind, heart, and body now to be found among us. We need not be afraid, in working for this, that we may make some irrevocable mistake, for the work will proceed gradually, and its achievements will themselves bear testimony to what aims and what methods are superior. At the same time, the very differences existing between the ideals of different participants in the enterprise, in lesser respects than those of the main objectives just mentioned, will aid in the maintenance of a helpful diversity, and this will enrich the whole.

It is true that only a small vanguard today would embark on germinal choice. But that is just as well, for the obstacles they must overcome serve to sift them so as to leave those with the clearest realization of human values as the main participants. Their examples will tend to guide the advances in salutary directions, and their achievements will tend to test and confirm these directions. By the time greater numbers join the enterprise, its objectives will have had an opportunity to become more widely appreciated. Moreover, the spread of education in such fundamentals as those of genetics and evolution may in the meantime have prepared a considerable part of the population to see things in the same light as the genetic pioneers.

At the same time, the banks of germinal material will have become greatly augmented, thus affording far wider ranges of choice. This will have come about not only by the deliberate gathering of this material for these purposes but also by the increased use of such storage, first, by persons wishing to protect their own germ cells from radiation and other mutagenic influences, and second, by persons who realize that sterilization by vasectomy, when complemented by storage, constitutes the most efficient means for the long-term control of conception. These additional stores would sometimes be found, in subsequent years, to contain material of unexpected value for germinal choice. The resulting greater availability of germinal material would allow the practice of germinal choice to become more generally spread among the population.

Along with all these developments, there will of course be increasing discussion of human values, and of how mankind may be bettered. This will involve people from the most diverse fields. We do not need to decide on the later aims now. But surely our successors, if man as a whole does succeed in raising himself by his bootstraps to a height equal to that of the highest now among us, will see that there is a long, long way still to go. They will not have to be so shortsighted in their aims as we, patterning their blueprints only on what now exists. For as the general level of life rises, its peaks will also become higher than those of today. Moreover, those who find themselves at greater heights can view more distant horizons. They can plan their courses further ahead. They can make increasing use of reason and imagination. Thus they will become more and more truly creators.

Certainly they will have genetic surgery. But they will not use it as a means of evading the use of suitable genetic material that is already available to them, just in order that they may maintain a mystique of promoting personal immortality for their idiosyncrasies through the exercise of natural procreation! They will use it along with germinal choice. These methods will not only complement each other but will, through subdivisions and refinements of each, broaden and touch each other. We may be choosing a whole chromosome set from here, a chromosome from there, a gene from a third source, and cause a directed mutation in another gene.

At the same time we will also use all available environmental methods of influencing favorably the organism's development and functioning: both what has sometimes been called euthenics and what Lederberg (14) has recently termed euphenics. J. D. Bernal's (15) speculations of 1929 in *The World, the Flesh, and the Devil* may be recommended as refreshing reading for persons who would like to know of some of the examples of euphenics that were even then foreseen as possibilities. However, it will be a long time before man himself can get along without genes (we need not quarrel about whether we would in that case call him man), and so long as genes are necessary he will benefit both by genetic betterment, that is, eugenics, and by extragenic betterment, that is, cultural evolution, including euthenics and euphenics.

It has been said that "sufficient to the day is the evil thereof." I would add that it is not sufficient for today just to contemplate the good of some distant tomorrow. Let us get all the good we can, by present means, for the generation immediately succeeding us and, through them, for subsequent generations in their turn, meanwhile working also to enhance our means of operation.

Certainly there is, in fields related to human genetic betterment, a vast amount of research to be conducted, over many generations. But the results of some of these lines of research can be more immediately applied, and these lines should not be neglected. For example, we sorely need better methods for finding out the effects of different conditions in producing or hindering mutations in human cells of different types and stages. This knowledge will enable us to protect germ cells better against mutagenesis. We need to follow up the studies on the possibility of preserving eggs indefinitely, to parallel what we can do with sperm. We need to find out the conditions necessary for causing cultures of immature germ cells to develop to maturity so that a minimum supply of immature germ cells, stored in deepfreeze, can be tapped repeatedly, so as to yield an unlimited supply of mature ones. We need to know how we can avoid having recombination of genes in inheritance when we wish to conserve the entire inheritance as such and, conversely, how to obtain recombination at will among cells in cultures.

All these problems might be termed proximate or nearby ones. They have not the depth and grandeur of work on the genetic code, or on genetic surgery. But they might lead to a rapid and enormous expansion of our means of getting better people. And these better people could work even more effectively than we on the more recondite problems that are far ahead of us.

And so I say, let us scientists recognize the respective values of our diverse approaches, and remain brothers. But let us work so that our successor-scientists will be both better brothers and better scientists. At the same time, let us help people in general to engage in a parallel advance. Then we can confidently entrust our successors with both germinal choice and genetic surgery.

Summary

The means exist right now of achieving a much greater, speedier, and more significant genetic improvement of the population, by the use of selection, than could be effected by the most sophisticated methods of treatment of the genetic material that might be available in the twenty-first century. The obstacles to carrying out such an improvement by selection are psychological ones, based on antiquated traditions from which we can emancipate ourselves, but the obstacles to doing so by treatment of the genetic material are substantive ones, rooted in the inherent difficulties of the physical, chemical, and biological situation.

To be sure, these material difficulties can increasingly be overcome, and the assault against them is bound to yield most rewarding and often unexpected benefits all along the way. But the road to a truly scientific control over the genetic basis of the most important human traits, such as general intelligence, social proclivities, and vigor, is an inordinately long one, for these traits depend on an enormous multitude of genes that interact in a superlatively complex fashion, and each individual receives from each of his parents a highly unique combination of these genes. Thus, supposing the means had actually been developed of making whatever genetic changes one wanted, it would still remain a Herculean task, requiring transcendent knowledge, to diagnose just what genetic "surgical" operations should be carried out in any given case in order to produce the development of the characteristics desired in that case. In view of these difficulties, it would be intellectually dishonest and morally reprehensible of us to exploit the hope of mankind's eventual success in this enterprise as an excuse for not giving our support in the meantime to the great re-educational process that could make possible, by means now physically available, a most significant advance in the genetic constitution of our species.

Bypassing the difficulties and the social mistakes of the old-style eugenics movements, the more positive approach offered by germinal choice utilizes the relatively new technique of preserving male reproductive cells for an unlimited period in a deeply frozen condition. The banks of germinal material that will thereby become available will include material derived from persons of outstanding gifts, intelligence, moral fiber, and physical fitness. In this way couples desiring to have in their own families one or more children who are especially likely to embody their own ideals of worth will be afforded a wide range of choice. They will be assisted by records of the lives and characteristics of the donors and of their relatives, and by counsel from diverse specialists, but the final choices will be their own and their participation will be entirely voluntary. It is to be expected that the use of this method will increase in the course of coming generations and will implement, on the genetic side, a great advance in human brotherhood, intelligence, and bodily vigor.

References

1. T. M. Sonneborn, *Amer. Inst. Biolog. Sci. Bull.,* **13** (2) :22, April, 1963.
2. M. Kondani, *Genetics,* **47**:965, 1962.
3. B. D. Hall and S. Spiegelman, *Proc. Nat. Acad. Sci. U.S.A.,* **47**:137, 1961, and S. Spiegelman, B. D. Hall, and R. Storck, *ibid.,* **47**:1135, 1961.
4. A. C. Clarke, *Industr. Res.,* 3 (5) :30, 1961.
5. H. J. Muller, *Out of the Night.* Vanguard Press, New York, 1935 and Gollancz, London, 1936.
6. H. J. Muller, *Excerpta Med.,* Intern. Cong. Ser. 32, p. E135, 1961.
7. H. Brewer, *Eugen. Rev.,* **27**:121, 1935.
   H. Brewer, *Lancet,* **1**:265, 1939.
8. J. S. Huxley, *Eugen. Rev.,* **54**:123, 1962.
9. A. Huxley, *Island.* Chatto and Windus, London, and Harper & Sons, New York, 1962.
10. A. S. Serebrowsky, *Abhandlungen der Abteilung zur Erforschung der Vererbung und Konstitution des Menschen am Mediz. Biol. Inst.,* Moscow, **1**:3, 1929.
11. H. Hoagland and G. Pincus, *J. Gen. Physiol.,* **25**:337, 1942.
12. H. Hoagland, *Sci. Monthly,* **56**:56, 1943.
13. J. K. Sherman, *Fertil. Steril.,* **14** (1) :49, 1963.
14. J. Lederberg, in: *Man and His Future* (ed. G. Wolstenholme), p. 263. J. & A. Churchill, London, 1963.
15. J. D. Bernal, *The World, the Flesh, and the Devil.* Kegan-Paul, Trench, Trubner & Co., London, and Dutton, New York, 1929.

Discussion—Part III

Dr. Luria

I know of no more difficult task than for a biologist to comment immediately after H. J. Muller. And certainly nobody would rashly seek an opportunity to disagree with him. This is not my intention. I think that the vision of human grandeur and of human progress that he has projected would cause anyone, who may have had qualms about interfering with the natural course of events, to see that the really natural course of events, the one dictated by the better nature of man, would be to follow in the direction that Muller has indicated. His discussion consists mainly of his marvelous vision of what germinal choice, the most positive form of eugenics, can accomplish for humanity and therefore for the whole world in which humanity is so dominant. I think that what Dr. Muller has stated about germinal choice versus negative selection is also extremely significant. The idea of negative selection is inevitably bound to the idea of imposed controls, whereas the idea of germinal choice has the exciting feature of an open-minded, clear decision made by individuals for their own good as well as for the general good.

I would like to comment briefly on Dr. Muller's discussion of the relative importance of what he has called genetic surgery versus parental selection. Much of the emphasis that has been placed here on genetic surgery by various men, including myself, may have created on the part of the readers the incorrect impression that a crash program or an intense concentration on methods of genetic surgery was advocated with the implication that such methods can accomplish what parental selection cannot, or can do the same but faster or better. This is definitely not so. Speaking for myself at least, what has been foremost in my mind since Dr. Sonneborn asked me to take part in this discussion has not been a feeling of optimism but one of tremendous fear of the potential dangers that genetic surgery, once it becomes feasible, can create if misapplied. I am convinced that the chances of improving human heredity by genetic surgery are much smaller than the chances of improving it by germinal choice. In addition, I believe that the difficulties of acceptance, based on psychological and sociological taboos, that stand in the way of germinal choice would be even more strongly in the way of genetic surgery. When I contemplate the tremendous advances that are being made in molecular biology and in various fields of genetics, I fear the possibility that a negative genetic surgery may become available and that society—and geneticists themselves—may not be preadapted to cope with the dangers.

I want to give just one example that came to my mind as I was listening to Dr. Muller. Suppose it were found in man, as has been found in a fruit fly, that there exists a virus that causes a tremendous sensitivity to carbon dioxide. For fruit flies that carry this virus, carbon dioxide becomes a deadly poison. It would in man, too. What would be the chance, if such a possibility suddenly arose in man, of avoiding such an infection and the resulting calamity? Someone could gain a tremendous control over humanity by spreading such a terrible object, thereby holding the power of life and death over a large number of human beings. This is an extreme and horrible example, almost science fiction matter, but it emphasizes the kind of thing that has been in my mind every time I have thought about the question of genetic surgery and engineering. The danger involved would be tremendous if such controls were to become available before society had learned to cope with them.

I believe that awareness of possibilities of this kind, if properly presented by geneticists together with the vision of the immense good that can come by a properly accepted and properly planned program of genetic choice, may very well make it much easier for humanity to accept the positive approach advocated so eloquently by Muller. Once genetics makes apparent both the tremendous dangers and the great potentialities for good, people may become more alert to, and more willing to accept, the enormous promises of this science.

*Dr. Sonneborn**

The critique of genetic surgery presented by Muller is literally unobjectionable. However, in spite of carefully qualified statements, the general impression given by it is that we can do little of con-

* Muller's customary masterly and impressive discussion climaxes this book, as it did the symposium on which the book is based. It was received with such enthusiasm by the audience that, after hurried consultation with some of the other speakers, we agreed it would be anticlimactic and quite undesirable to throw it open for general discussion, an agreement that seemed all the more wise in view of the lateness of the evening hour and the fact that we had

sequence with genetic surgery until we have very extensive knowledge of the details of man's genetic equipment and of how given changes in it would interact with the rest of a person's genome. As he states, such extensive knowledge will hardly be available in the twenty-first century, if ever. Indeed, the magnitude of the task is so fantastically great that it is hard to imagine it will ever be completed unless entirely new and presently unforeseen methods of analysis become available. With this it is hard to disagree.

One can, however, disagree with the point of view that little of consequence can be accomplished until such knowledge is available. Muller is careful to qualify his statements so as to cover this possibility, but he does so in such a way as to minimize its importance. He refers to it as restricted to empirical procedures lacking a sound basis in knowledge and therefore subject to risk of making unforeseeable and presumably tragic mistakes. Granting that this is true, it is nevertheless also true that such empirical procedures could be of great importance and value with man, as they have been with microorganisms, and that the risk of tragic mistakes need not be excessive.

Consider for instance the form of genetic surgery based on transformation by extracted DNA. It is not at all necessary to know the chromosome or the nucleotide involved in the trait to which the genetic surgery is to be applied. Indeed, to this day very little is known about the positions or constitutions of the genes in the pneumonia bacterium, yet amazing control of transformation has been achieved in it. In spite of well-recognized technical difficulties, not insurmountable, the same semiblind selective approach might be developed for human cells, even for cells that give rise to germ cells. Replacing such selected germ cell progenitors back in the body from which they were taken could lead to much control of human heredity.

Muller correctly insists that the most important human traits depend on the cumulative action of many genes, often individually relatively minor side effects of genes with different major effects, but his argument that this virtually nullifies the possibility of effective genetic surgery can be contested. As he states, the gene for each

---

been in almost continuous session morning, afternoon, and evening for a whole day. Only Dr. Luria, who had earlier been asked particularly to be prepared to comment on Dr. Muller's paper, was called upon to speak. He made the preceding statement. Other members of the panel, however, asked the convener-editor to write a more extensive comment on Muller's discussion and include it in the book. With Dr. Muller's consent, this was done.

subnormal or defective trait has multiple deleterious effects. Hence, its empirical replacement by a normal or favorable gene in the manner outlined above not only achieves normality for the major conspicuous trait but also some measure of improvement for all or most of the minor multiple effects. Thus, selection for improvement in multiple gene traits by transformation or by other methods of genetic surgery should lead step by step to continuing improvement.

In this respect, the same arguments Muller uses so effectively for parental selection could be applied to genetic surgery. He holds that parental selection, although empirical and not based on precise knowledge of the genes involved—of either their location, composition, number, or mode of action—would be effective in a small but cumulative way that in the long run would be telling. In exactly the same way, genetic surgery would be empirical but also slowly and cumulatively telling. The fact that all possible viable forms of genes now exist in the world population is as useful for genetic surgery (using them as sources of transforming DNA, for instance) as it is for parental selection. And it is subject to the same limitations—knowing and finding the desired genes and gene combinations The multiple-factor basis of the most important traits is a difficulty in the one method as well as in the other.

The real difference in effectiveness between the methods of genetic surgery and parental selection depends on the fact that genetic surgery deals with cells and parental selection deals with individuals. How, for instance, can cells be selected for high intelligence? This sort of selection depends on discovery of the basic biochemical properties underlying high intelligence before one could select for them at the cellular level. Selecting DNA from the cells of individuals with high intelligence and applying it to the germ cells of individuals with lower intelligence as an empirical procedure would be of little use unless one had some means of selecting the exposed cells that had acquired the desired DNA. As yet we do not know how to do this. Success depends not on detailed knowledge of the genetic basis of intelligence, but on its biochemical basis. The latter is not now known except in a few cases of extreme defectiveness. However, it would seem to be much more readily discoverable than the corresponding detailed genetic knowledge. I venture to predict that it will be possible in the foreseeable future to obtain much detailed biochemical knowledge of the differences between cells from highly intelligent and average individuals. Whether such knowledge would make it possible to select desired cellular transformants for empirical but highly successful genetic surgery then depends on whether some decisive aspects of high intellectual potential are related to cellular interrelations that may not be discoverable from study of single cells, as well they may. The same considerations apply to other complex traits.

It would then appear that much could be achieved by genetic surgery as well as by parental selection, using in both cases empirical procedures without the need for detailed genetic knowledge. In principle the same biological limitations now exist for the one as for the other method, and the psychosociological limitations are not very different either. However, one must agree with Muller's insistence that substantive difficulties at present stand in the way of surgery, while the means are now available for using parental selection. But in view of the possibilities of semiblind empirical approaches, these substantive difficulties are greatly reduced. Concerted efforts to characterize biochemically the cellular differences corresponding to individual hereditary difference, to culture and reimplant germ cells from and into one and the same individual, and to develop methods for DNA incorporation followed by selection based on biochemical criteria would go a long way toward bringing genetic surgery to the point of practical application.

In self-defence, now, I must say that in previous publications and lectures I have in general taken toward genetic surgery a point of view similar to Muller's. I too have emphasized its difficulties and agreed with the immediate availability of some form of old-fashioned or more modern eugenics. My comments on Muller's paper are not intended to minimize the difficulties of the one or the immediate possibilities of the other, but merely to question whether the prospects for genetic surgery are as limited, dim, and remote as Muller's statement of the situation might lead one to believe.

The purpose of this book is to present both sides of the subject as effectively as possible with criticism and countercriticism in the hope that the thoughtful and careful reader will see in the end both the possibilities and the limitations, as well as sense the great underlying moral, ethical, and social issues, of both approaches to the improvement of man's future lot. As such, this book should long remain a significant contribution to what should become a continuing reappraisal of the situation in the years ahead.